THE SLIDE RULE

Principles and Applications

The SLIDE RULE

Principles and Applications

JOSEPH NORMAN ARNOLD

Associate Professor of General Engineering
Purdue University

PRENTICE-HALL, INC.

Englewood Cliffs, N.J.

PREFACE

Mechanical principle and mathematical theory are emphasized in this book. All the traditional principles along with features of recently developed slide rules are discussed. Distinctive characteristics are the representation of alternative scale arrangements and suggestions for recognizing the nature of scales and methods of operation on any slide rule, regardless of scale marking. This approach leads to a better grasp of underlying principles and, consequently, greater facility.

Large parts of Chapters 1 and 2, which make up nearly half the book, have been written for the person with no knowledge of algebra. Greater familiarity with mathematics is necessary in order to use the trigonometric scales and to carry out logarithmic operations. Thus, Chapters 3 and 4 assume an understanding of trigonometry and logarithms.

Obviously, each reader should have his own slide rule and should use it to follow the examples. A sufficient number of problems should be solved to develop speed and confidence; not all of the practice problems should be from the one thousand and more number problems of Part I—some should be selected from the practical problems of Part II. The problems on preparation of graphs, at the very end of several chapters, will appeal to many users. Answers to alternate rows of problems in Part I are provided in the Appendix.

An additional feature is the summary at the end of each chapter in Part I, which will aid in review after the study of the chapter has been completed. Also, if the use of the slide rule is discontinued for a time, the summaries will provide a ready reference for regaining skill.

The author is indebted to Eugene Dietzgen Company, Keuffel and Esser Company, Pickett and Eckel, Incorporated, and Frederick Post Company for providing the catalog illustrations of slide rules in the Appendix.

The work of M. H. Bolds and W. E. Thomas, who prepared most of the drawings, is appreciated. A number of colleagues helped with the practical problems of Part II: the assistance of Professors A. A. Alberts, F. J. Bogardus, Herschel Hunt, M. B. Scott, and I. Walerstein is gratefully acknowledged. And finally, Professor W. E. Fontaine helped set up the general pattern and arrangement of the book in anticipation of co-authorship, which it was not possible to carry through. He also provided a considerable number of the problems. His counsel and assistance are deeply appreciated.

West Lafayette, Indiana

J. N. Arnold

TABLE OF CONTENTS

Part II. Applications of the Slide Rule to Various Fields

PART I

The Basic Slide Rule Principle

Typical Examples and Exercises

Regardless of its shape or size, any slide rule performs its mathematical wizardry by subtracting, adding, or equating lengths on functional scales; the particular relationship solved depends upon the type of functional scale and the operation to be performed, whether subtraction, addition, or equating of lengths.

Log scales having equal cycle lengths are the subject of Chapter 1. Log scales with simple cycle-length ratios of $2:1$, $3:1$, $3:2$, are discussed in Chapter 2. The use of log sin scales and log tan scales and variations of them, along with simple log scales, are topics in Chapter 3. The use of LogLog scales and uniform scales along with the log scales are included in Chapter 4.

These few types of functional scales will solve a tremendous number of practical computations, but they do not exhaust the possibilities by any means. Other types of functional scales, in infinite variety, can be made —and many are useful.

The scale equations of the Appendix, Art. A.2, and references on special slide rules* should help one who masters Part I to enlarge his knowledge and understanding of slide rules.

---

* Hoelscher, R. P., J. N. Arnold, and S. H. Pierce, *Graphic Aids in Engineering Computation*, Chap. 6 ("Special Slide Rules"). New York: McGraw-Hill Book Co., 1952.

Chapter

1

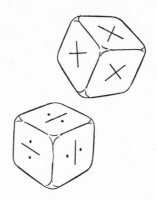

DIVISION, MULTIPLICATION,
AND RELATED TOPICS

1.1. Types of Slide Rules. Slide rules are made in a variety of shapes, including cylindrical, circular, flat spiral, and straight. The straight slide rule is much more commonly used than the other shapes, so this book is limited to discussion of the straight slide rule.

The straight slide rule consists of three principal parts as shown by the diagrammatic pictures, Figs. 1.1 and 1.2. These parts are: the frame (or base), the slide, and the runner (or glass). The hairline is a scribed mark on the glass.

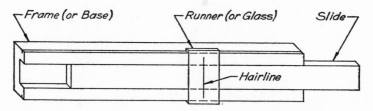

Fig. 1.1. Components of Mannheim-Type Slide Rule

The two forms of straight slide rules in common use are the duplex type, Fig. 1.2, having scales on both front and back, and the Mannheim type, Fig. 1.1, with a solid back to the frame, and therefore having scales on one side only. But some Mannheim-type slide rules do have scales on both faces of the slide; the scales on the back of the slide may be used by withdrawing the slide and turning it over, or by reading opposite a gauge mark or scribed glass on the end of the frame.

The beginner with a slide rule often experiences a feeling of hopelessness when he notes that there are some twenty scales on a LogLog slide rule, all of which are strange and meaningless when first examined. However, by taking up the mathematical operations and associated slide rule scales one at a time, confidence and skill in the use of the slide rule can be developed.

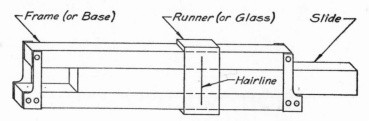

Fig. 1.2.   Components of Duplex-Type Slide Rule

1.2. Mechanical Principle of the Slide Rule.   The remarkable, but fundamentally simple, feature of the slide rule is that it performs division, multiplication, and several other mathematical operations by one or sometimes a sequence of the following basic mechanical operations:

    a. Subtract lengths
    b. Add lengths
    c. Equate lengths

Most of the slide rule scales are not uniformly graduated.   However, the mechanical principle is shown in very simple fashion by the slide rule of

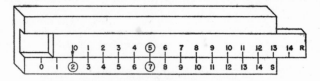

Fig. 1.3.   Slide Rule for Subtraction or Addition

Operation: Set value of R opposite value of S:
   Read $D = S - R$ opposite arrow
Example: $7 - 5 = 2$
   Set arrow at D
   Opposite value of R read $S = D + R$
Example: $2 + 5 = 7$

Fig. 1.3, which has uniformly graduated scales.   A slide rule of this form having more and finer graduations could be used to add, subtract, or equate over a much wider range of numbers than the few shown in Fig. 1.3.

A great variety of slide rules have been devised in the three hundred years since the first one for performing division and multiplication was prepared, but the mechanical principle of operation is unchanged. All straight slide rules operate by adding, subtracting, or equating lengths in the manner of Fig. 1.3—but using scales which are non-uniformly graduated.

If one clearly understands the mechanical principle and the way it relates to the mathematical principle, it is possible to identify the suitable scales on any slide rule to use for division or multiplication; also, the method of operation is easily devised.

1.3. Mathematical Principle of the Slide Rule for Division and Multiplication. It is not necessary to understand the mathematical theory in order to use a slide rule, but if the theory is understood, it is easier to develop skill in slide rule use, and easier to learn new applications.

Logarithms of numbers underlie division and multiplication as performed with the slide rule. Logarithms are explained in algebraic terms in the Summary, page 48. Their use is described in words as follows:

DIVISION: *If the logarithm of one number is subtracted from the logarithm of another, the difference is the logarithm of the quotient.*

MULTIPLICATION: *If the logarithm of the first factor is added to the logarithm of a second factor, the sum is equal to the logarithm of the product.*

A selected few numbers and their approximate logarithms are given here in the form of a table. The logarithm principle may be verified easily by using these table values to check a few examples, such as: $40/8 = 5$; $20/5 = 4$; $5 \times 6 = 30$; $2 \times 3 = 6$; and others.

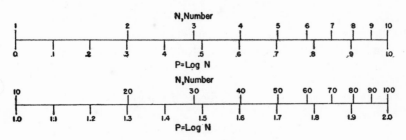

Fig. 1.4.   Graphic Logarithm of Numbers
Major Graduation Only Shown

The same table information is presented in graphic form in Fig. 1.4, where the non-uniform character of the logarithmic scale is perhaps more clearly evident. From 1 to 2 is about 30 per cent of the distance from

1 to 10.   The distance from 8 to 9 and the distance from 9 to 10 are much less than the distance from 1 to 2.

No., N	$p = \log N$	No., N	$p = \log N$
1	0.000	10	1.000
2	0.301	20	1.301
3	0.477	30	1.477
4	0.602	40	1.602
5	0.699	50	1.699
6	0.778	60	1.778
7	0.845	70	1.845
8	0.903	80	1.903
9	0.954	90	1.954
10	1.000	100	2.000

$$\begin{aligned} \log 40 &= 1.602 \\ -\log 8 &= -0.903 \\ \hline \log 5 &= 0.699 \end{aligned} \qquad \begin{aligned} \log 2 &= 0.301 \\ \log 3 &= 0.477 \\ \hline \log 6 &= 0.778 \end{aligned}$$

It is possible to use any number as a base for logarithms, but only two numbers are in common use, 10 and e.   Throughout Chapters 1, 2, and 3, 10 is understood to be the base unless otherwise noted.   In Chapter 4 both e and 10 are used.

1.4. Recognition of Scales for Division and Multiplication.   In view of the foregoing explanation of the mechanical and mathematical principle, it should be evident that there are two requirements for a slide rule to perform division or multiplication.   There must be two logarithmic scales, one movable relative to the other; the cycle length, or distance from 1 to 10, must be the same for both scales.

Logarithmic scales can be recognized by observing if the distance from 1 to 2 is 30 per cent of the distance from 1 to 10, as in Fig. 1.4.   Also, the distance from 1 to 2 must equal the distance from 2 to 4.   In fact the distance on a particular logarithmic scale between any two numbers having a ratio of 2:1 is the same.   Observation of this distance between numbers 1 and 2, or 2 and 4, or 5 and 10 may be called the "ratio test for logarithmic scales."

Observation also will readily indicate if the cycle lengths for two logarithmic scales are equal.

Although the earliest form of slide rule consisted of two marked sticks placed side by side unconfined by any frame and without an indicator glass, many commercial slide rules now have more than one pair of scales which may be used for division or multiplication.

The beginner may find it helpful to apply the ratio test and cycle length test to his slide rule in an attempt to identify all pairs of scales which might be used for division or multiplication.

1.5. Commercial Slide Rules.[1] It would take more pages than can be used here for the purpose to describe in detail the many different forms of straight slide rules which have been made and sold. Therefore, it is intended to limit the specific information in this book to a few of the widely used slide rules. Illustrations of several commercial slide rules are shown in the Appendix, pages 182–189, along with a table of data summarizing the properties and uses of some of their scales. At various places throughout the book, reference is made to the Appendix illustrations and practical features of the various slide rules are shown.

Thus, by applying the 2:1 ratio test of Art. 1.4, it may be observed that each of the various commercial slide rules has 5 or more logarithmic scales. In particular, the reader may verify that the Mannheim-type slide rule, Fig. A.1, has logarithmic scales labelled A, B, C, D, and CI. The mated pairs on slide and frame are A and B, C and D.

The LogLog Duplex Deci-Trig slide rule of Fig. A.3 has logarithmic scales marked DF, CF, CIF, CI, C, D, on the front, while on the back the scales marked K, A, B, and D are logarithmic.

The Deci-LogLog slide rule is shown in Fig. A.5, from which it may be determined by the 2:1 ratio test that there are logarithmic scales marked DF, CF, CI, C, D, DI, $\sqrt{\ }$, $\sqrt[3]{\ }$, DF/$_M$, CF/$_M$. Of this group the mated pairs are C and D, CF and DF, CI and DI, CF/$_M$ and DF/$_M$.

The other slide rules shown, Figs. A.2, A.4, A.6, A.7, and A.8, are much like one or another of these three in the arrangement and labelling of the logarithmic scales. They differ from the three first-mentioned principally in the nature or placement of other scales.

1.6. Graduation of Scales. A knowledge of which scales to use and an ability to read the scales are the first steps in learning to use the slide rule. The non-uniform nature of the logarithmic scale makes it slightly more difficult to read than the ordinary footrule or yardstick, but the placing of numbers at major graduation marks and the use of different lengths of graduation marks for subdivisions are similar to the footrule. The logarithmic scale is graduated in decimal parts in contrast to the 1/2, 1/4, and 1/8 often found on the footrule. That is, the slide rule graduations are spaced 1/2, 1/5, or 1/10 units.

The scales marked C and D are most frequently used for division and multiplication; C and D scales are shown on all of the selected commercial slide rules, and this marking is very common on other makes of slide rules not illustrated. It is, therefore, convenient to begin with a consideration of the graduation plan for C and D scales.

The C and D scales on all slide rules are numbered at the major graduation marks corresponding to the numbers 1, 2, 3—on up to 10. The

---

[1] For convenience and brevity the term "commercial" slide rule is used throughout the book to refer to a mass-produced slide rule for general purpose calculations.

interval between each two major graduations is subdivided into 10 parts; on the three-section picture, Fig. 1.5, these are denoted as minor graduations. Almost all commercial slide rules carry small numbers at the minor graduations between 1 and 2, but not for any other interval. The major number is omitted from these. That is, the small 1, 2, 3, and so on, near the left end of the C and D scales of Fig. 1.5 represent 1.1, 1.2, 1.3, and so forth, up to 1.9.

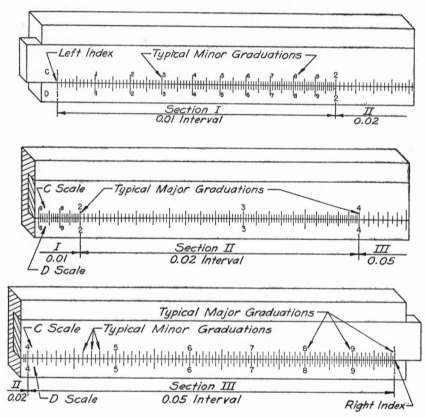

Fig. 1.5. Nature of Scale Graduation
10-inch Log Scale

It will be observed that the minor graduation strokes are made as long as or longer than the strokes for major graduations and the 0.5 marks are made especially long.

Between the numbers 1 and 2 on 10-inch slide rules, it is the usual practice to make 10 subdivisions between the minor graduations; thus, the interval between finest graduations represents 0.01, as shown in Section I, Fig. 1.5.

Between the numbers 2 and 4 it is customary to place 5 subdivisions between each minor graduation. In this section of the scale, the interval between finest graduations represents twice 0.01, or 0.02 (Section II, Fig. 1.5).

On a 5-inch pocket slide rule, fewer graduations must be used if the scale is to be readable. On 20-inch slide rules more graduations are possible than on the more common 10-inch slide rule, with a corresponding increase in accuracy. Regardless of the length, the general plan of subdivision on all logarithmic scales is to place the finest graduation marks at 1/2, 1/5, 1/10, or 1/20 of the minor interval. Counting of graduation marks in a minor interval at different portions of the scale enables one to find the subdivision interval on slide rules different from those shown here.

Slide rule settings represented by graduation marks can be made quite accurately. Numbers between graduation marks also can be set or read closely by observing the numerical value of the finest interval and estimating the proportionate distance between marks.

Several examples of setting numbers on the D scale are proposed, described, and illustrated in Figs. 1.6 through 1.8. These examples intentionally avoid decimal point difficulties, thus focusing attention on the scale reading. The illustrations also omit other scales than D and represent a crude form of the frame for simplicity and convenience of preparation.

It is suggested that the reader attempt to make the setting on his slide rule without reference to the illustration and description. After making the setting a comparison with the description and illustration should reveal any errors; this procedure should lead to more rapid correction of faults in scale reading.

EXAMPLE 1.6A. Set 3.12 on D. This setting is approximately half way along the D scale. One minor graduation to the right of 3 represents 3.1. The finest graduation interval represents 0.02 in this portion of the scale. The setting for 3.12 is one graduation to the right of 3.10. See Fig. 1.6.

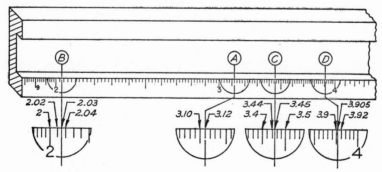

Fig. 1.6. Scale Setting for Examples 1.6A: 3.12; 1.6B: 2.03; 1.6C: 3.45; 1.6D: 3.905

EXAMPLE 1.6B. Set 2.03 on D. This setting is approximately one-third of the way along the D scale. The finest graduation interval represents 0.02 in this portion; therefore, 2.02 is one graduation to the right of 2. The position for 2.03 is estimated midway between 2.02 and 2.04. See Fig. 1.6.

EXAMPLE 1.6C. Set 3.45 on D. This setting is approximately midway along the D scale. The position for 3.45 is estimated midway between 3.44 and 3.46. See Fig. 1.6.

EXAMPLE 1.6D. Set 3.905 on D. This setting is approximately three-fifths of the way along the D scale, and is estimated at one-fourth of the way from 3.9 to 3.92. See Fig. 1.6.

EXAMPLE 1.6E. Set 4.98 on D. This setting is approximately two-thirds of the way along the D scale. The finest graduation interval

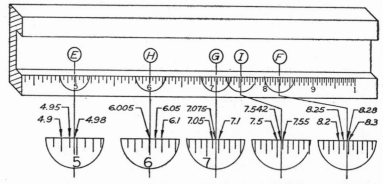

Fig. 1.7. Scale Settings for Examples 1.6E: 4.98; 1.6F: 8.28; 1.6G: 7.075; 1.6H: 6.005; 1.61I: 7.542

represents 0.05 in this portion; therefore, 4.95 is one graduation to the left of 5; the position for 4.98 is estimated at three-fifths of the way from 4.95 to 5. See Fig. 1.7.

EXAMPLE 1.6F. Set 8.28 on D. This setting is approximately nine-tenths of the way along the D scale. The second minor graduation from 8 represents 8.2; the third minor graduation represents 8.3. The finest graduation interval represents 0.05 in this portion; therefore, 8.25 is the graduation midway between 8.2 and 8.3; the position for 8.28 is estimated at three-fifths of the way from 8.25 to 8.3. See Fig. 1.7.

EXAMPLE 1.6G. Set 7.075 on D. This setting is approximately five-sixths of the way along the D scale, and is estimated at midway between 7.05 and 7.1. See Fig. 1.7.

EXAMPLE 1.6H. Set 6.005 on D. This setting is approximately three-fourths of the way along the D scale, and is estimated at one-tenth of the way from 6 to 6.05. See Fig. 1.7.

EXAMPLE 1.6I. Set 7.542 on D. This setting is approximately nine-tenths of the way along the D scale, and the position of 7.542 is estimated at four-fifths of the way from 7.5 to 7.55. See Fig. 1.7.

EXAMPLE 1.6J. Set 1.32 on D. This setting is approximately one-eighth of the way along the D scale. The third minor graduation from the left, marked with a small 3, represents 1.3. The finest graduation interval represents 0.01 in this portion; therefore, 1.32 is two graduations from 1.3. See Fig. 1.8.

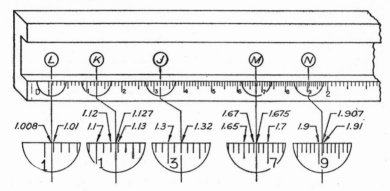

Fig. 1.8. Scale Settings for Examples 1.6J: 1.32; 1.6K: 1.27; 1.6L: 1.008, 1.6M: 1.675; 1.6N: 1.907

EXAMPLE 1.6K. Set 1.127 on D. This setting is less than one-tenth of the way along the D scale. The first minor graduation from the left, marked with a small 1, represents 1.1; the second finest graduation from 1.1 represents 1.12; the third finest graduation from 1.1 represents 1.13; the position for 1.127 is estimated at seven-tenths of the distance between 1.12 and 1.13. See Fig. 1.8.

EXAMPLE 1.6L. Set 1.008 on D. This setting is very near the left end of the D scale, and the position for 1.008 is estimated at four-fifths of the distance from 1 to 1.01. See Fig. 1.8.

EXAMPLE 1.6M. Set 1.675 on D. This setting is approximately one-fourth of the way along the D scale, and the position for 1.675 is estimated at midway between 1.67 and 1.68. See Fig. 1.8.

EXAMPLE 1.6N. Set 1.907 on D. This setting is approximately one-fourth of the way along the D scale, and 1.907 is estimated at seven-tenths of the way from 1.9 to 1.91. See Fig. 1.8.

1.7. Problems in Scale Reading. A set of scale reading problems in which various numbers are merely set on the C or D scales cannot be checked for correctness except by having someone familiar with a slide rule examine each setting.

The plan used for this set of problems enables the reader to check his own setting or reading against answers in the back of the book. If the hairline is set to a number on the C scale and the number which appears on the CI scale under the hairline is read, the reading provides a check on the correctness.

It will be observed that the "CI" scale, standing for C Inverted, is just like the C scale except for being reversed in direction. That is, the

1, 2, and 3 on the CI scale are at the right-hand end, and increasing to the left. The graduations on CI are of identically the same nature as those on the C and D scales.

Set the hairline to the number in the table on the C scale; read on the CI scale.

	1A	1B	1C	1D	1E
a*	2.00	4.00	1.10	1.01	1.005
b	1.92	1.29	2.63	8.02	9.28
c	8.00	7.95	6.06	6.60	4.11
d	1.015	2.04	4.016	6.54	2.31
e	1.30	4.27	3.16	9.40	2.12
f	2.585	1.71	3.06	1.363	2.74
g	5.71	1.40	2.94	2.175	5.10
h	1.063	4.20	6.17	8.20	6.71

*Answers for every other row of problems in Part I are provided in the Appendix.

1.8. Manipulation of the Slide Rule. Speed and accuracy with the slide rule require, among other things, smooth and effortless control of the slide and runner. For this purpose the slide rule must be properly adjusted. The beginner, because he has difficulty in controlling the slide rule, sometimes concludes that it requires adjustment, whereas the primary need may be for additional practice to overcome his awkwardness.

This article and the illustrations offer advice to the beginner on how to hold and control the slide rule, assuming it is properly adjusted. If, after practice, adjustment still seems to be required, page 192 of the Appendix should be consulted.

Accurate setting of the slide can be attained best by having two hands in contact with the slide as shown in Fig. 1.9 or Fig. 1.10. The thumb or

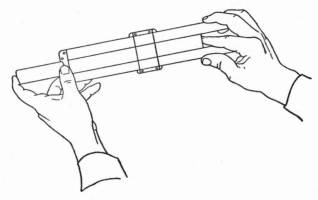

Fig. 1.9. Holding the Slide Rule: Fingers Controlling Motion

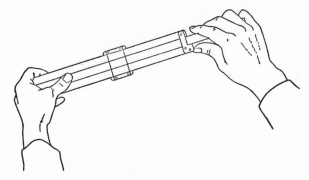

Fig. 1.10.   Holding the Slide Rule: Thumb Controlling Motion

finger of the left hand working against the motion of the slide being made by the other hand provides smooth motion with very little muscular tenseness.

Of course it is necessary to avoid squeezing the two bars of the frame, on a duplex rule particularly.   The squeezing will cause the slide to bind, and thus make setting the slide more difficult.

When the slide position is nearly centered in the frame, it is more convenient to use the forefingers on the slide as shown in Fig. 1.9 rather then the thumbs as shown in Fig. 1.10.

Two-hand control of the runner in the same manner, with one hand opposed to the other, is often helpful.   However, it is usually satisfactory to move the runner with one hand as shown in Fig. 1.11.

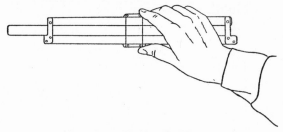

Fig. 1.11.   Moving the Runner

1.9. Introduction to Division, C and D Scales.   Art. 1.3 demonstrates the principle of logarithms by means of simple examples, and calls attention to the fact that the logarithmic principle is the basis for performing division using the C and D scales.

> LOGARITHMIC PRINCIPLE FOR DIVISION: *If the logarithm of one number,* M, *is subtracted from the logarithm of another,* N, *the result is the logarithm of the quotient,* Q.

In consequence of this principle, the usual procedure for operating the C and D scales of the slide rule to perform division is:

Set the hairline of the runner to the numerator on the D scale
Move the slide to place the denominator on C beneath the
  hairline
Read the quotient on D opposite the index (or 1)
See the diagram, Fig. 1.12

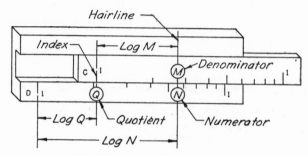

Fig. 1.12. Division Principle

$\log N - \log M = \log Q$; or $N/M = Q$

In order to focus attention on the method of operation several examples
are presented which intentionally avoid decimal point difficulties. It is
suggested that the reader attempt to solve these examples using his own
slide rule; thus, the examples will provide additional practice in scale
reading and in manipulation, as well as aid in fixing the method of operation more clearly in mind. Again, a simplified but workable form of
slide rule is shown in the illustrations.

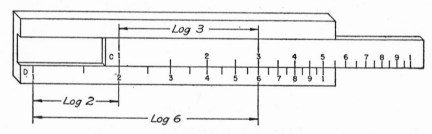

Fig. 1.13. Division: Partially Graduated Scales

Example 1.9A: $\log 6 - \log 3 = \log 2$; or $6/3 = 2$

EXAMPLE 1.9A.   Calculate 6/3 using C and D scales.

Solution: Set the hairline to 6 on D
        Place 3 on C beneath the hairline
        Read 2 on D opposite the 1 on the end of the C scale
        See Fig. 1.13 for setting

EXAMPLE 1.9B.   Calculate 7/4 using C and D scales.

Solution: Set the hairline to 7 on D
      Place 4 on C beneath the hairline
      Read 1.75 on D opposite the index

EXAMPLE 1.9C.   Calculate 8/5 using C and D scales.

Solution: Set the hairline to 8 on D
      Place 5 on C beneath the hairline
      Read 1.6 on D opposite the index

EXAMPLE 1.9D.   Calculate 4.16/3.14 using C and D scales.

Solution: Set the hairline to 4.16 on D
      Place 3.14 on C beneath the hairline
      Read 1.325 on D opposite the index

Because the setting of 4.16 and reading the answer require estimating
between graduation marks, the last digit in the answer may be estimated
as 6, or 4, or 7.   In most computations, variations of this amount, a fraction of a per cent, are of no importance.

EXAMPLE 1.9E.   Calculate 3.59/1.342 using C and D scales.

Solution: Set the hairline to 3.59 on D
      Place 1.342 on C beneath the hairline
      Read 2.675 on D opposite the index

The variation in answers in the last digit obtained by different persons,
or by the same person at different times, may be slightly greater in this
example than in Example 1.9D, because all numbers must be estimated.
However, if the example is carefully solved all answers should lie between
2.670 and 2.680.

EXAMPLE 1.9F.   Calculate 17/7 using C and D scales.   Fig. 1.4 shows
that the distances on a logarithmic scale from 1 to 2, 10 to 20, or any two

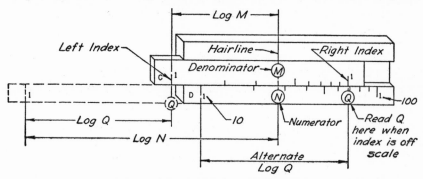

Fig. 1.14.   Division Principle: Alternate Index

$\log N - \log M = \log Q$; or $N/M = Q$

numbers with the same ratio is the same. It is possible, therefore, for the D scale to represent numbers from 10 to 100, from 0.1 to 1, or from 1000 to 10,000 provided the decimal point position is determined separately.

Solution: Set the hairline to 1.7 on D (representing 17)

Place 7 on C beneath the hairline

Read 2.43 on D opposite the index—in this case the index is the 1 at the right-hand end of the C scale

Fig. 1.14 illustrates the principle of interchanging indices; Fig. 1.15 illustrates this example.

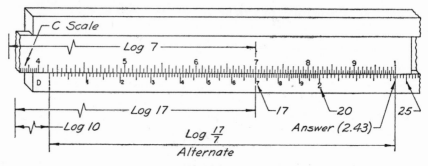

Fig. 1.15.   Division: Alternate Index

Example 1.9F: 17/7 = 2.43

1.10. Decimal Point Location.   It would be possible to make a slide rule on which the numbers complete with decimal point could be set and read.   If one attempted on such a slide rule to cover the range of numbers from 1 to 1,000,000 with the accuracy of the standard C and D scales, a slide rule six times as long would be required—that is, 5 feet long as compared with 10 inches for the usual C and D scales, Fig. 1.16. Also, for any problem in which one of the given factors or the answer were greater than 1,000,000 or less than 1, a still longer slide rule would be required.

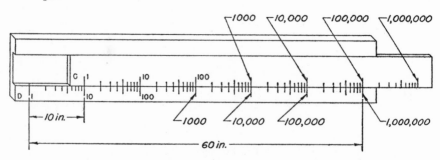

Fig. 1.16.   Model of Slide Rule to Read Decimal Point Position

If the decimal point is determined independently of the slide rule, a single logarithmic cycle (1 to 10) is sufficient for all problems in division and multiplication.   And although decimal point determination initially appears to be quite a chore, a systematic method and practice make it very little trouble.

Several methods[2] for placing the decimal point have been devised.   It is not intended to include all of these methods because to do so might be more confusing than helpful.   Experiments in teaching slide rule operation by different methods have shown that about one third of the errors of beginners occur in misplacing the decimal point.[3]   Also, a considerable reduction in the number of errors results if instruction is given in the "standard number" method.   This method and one which may be called the "similar simple number scheme" are presented here.

The terms "standard number" and "correction number" as used in decimal point placement require definition.   A few examples of application to division problems will make the definitions more meaningful.

STANDARD NUMBER: A "standard number" is defined as a number written in such manner that the decimal point follows the first digit of the significant figures.   Examples of numbers written in the usual form and in standard form are:

Usual Form	Standard Form	Correction No.
5280	5.280 × 1000	3
327	3.27 × 100	2
27	2.7 × 10	1
0.0316	3.16 × 0.01	−2
0.0025	2.5 × 0.001	−3

For the purpose of placing the decimal point in slide rule computation it is not necessary to write out each number in standard form.   A short-cut method of merely counting the number of places the decimal point must be moved to form a standard number is equally effective and more rapid.

CORRECTION NUMBER: The number of places the decimal point must be moved is called the "correction number."   The correction number is considered positive if the decimal point is moved to the left to form a standard number; if the decimal point must be moved to the right to form a standard number the correction number is negative.   The reader familiar with logarithms will observe that the correction number is merely the characteristic of the logarithm of the number.   Correction number seems to be a less frightening name for the reader unacquainted with logarithms.

---

[2] For one of the methods not described here see Harris, C. O., *Slide Rule Simplified*, pages 52, 70.   Chicago: American Technical Society, 1943.

[3] Shuster, Carl N., *A Study of the Problems in Teaching the Slide Rule*.   New York: Columbia University Press, 1940.

SIMILAR SIMPLE NUMBER SCHEME: Rounding off the given numbers to form numbers having one digit and zeros, then using cancellation and mental arithmetic to approximate the answer will determine the decimal point position. Even in using the standard number method for placing the decimal point cancellation and mental arithmetic are necessary.

EXAMPLE 1.10A. Calculate 9265/24. Rounding the numbers:

$$\frac{9265}{24} = \frac{9000}{20} \text{ approx.} = 400 \text{ approx.}$$

The reading from the slide rule is 3.86; hence the answer is 386.

Using the standard number form, and carrying it out completely:

$$\frac{9265}{24} = \frac{9.265 \times 1000}{2.4 \times 10} = \frac{9.265}{2.4} \times \frac{1000}{10} = \frac{9.265}{2.4} \times 100$$

Again

$$\frac{9}{2} = 4 \text{ approx.}$$

Therefore, the answer is approximately 4×100, or 400.

The four steps in applying the short-cut method to this example are:

1. Write the numerator as a standard number with its correction number above; write the denominator as a standard number with its correction number below.

2. Algebraically subtract the correction number of the denominator from the correction number of the numerator, and write this quantity above the space for the answer.

3. Mentally approximate the division of the standard numbers, and place the decimal point in the answer in accordance with this mental approximation.

4. Express the standard number answer with its correction number in the usual form by moving the decimal point the number of places indicated by the resultant correction number.

Using the short-cut method, 9265 becomes a standard number if the decimal point is moved three places to the left; the correction number is then $+3$. For the denominator, 24, the correction number is $+1$. The resultant correction number is:

$$3 - 1 = 2$$

The notation of the correction numbers may be easily made as follows:

$$\frac{9265}{24} = \frac{\overset{+3}{9.265}}{\underset{+1}{2.4}} = \overset{+2}{3.86} = 386$$

EXAMPLE 1.10B.   Calculate 5.71/0.00271.   Rounding off:

$$\frac{6}{0.003} = 2000$$

Since the slide rule reading is 2.11, the answer is 2110.   By the standard number method:

$$\frac{5.71}{0.00271} = \frac{\overset{0}{5.71}}{\underset{-3}{2.71}} = \overset{+3}{2.11} = 2110$$

since

$$0 - (-3) = +3$$

EXAMPLE 1.10C.   Calculate 0.241/41.5.   By the standard number method:

$$\frac{0.241}{41.5} = \frac{\overset{-1}{2.41}}{\underset{+1}{4.15}} = \overset{-2}{0.581} = 0.00581$$

$$-1 - (+1) = -2$$

It should be observed that for the simple numbers

$$\frac{2}{4} = 0.5$$

not 5, and the net correction number of -2 is applied to the 0.581, thus making the answer 0.00581.

1.11. Division, C and D Scales.   This article includes some examples slightly more difficult than those in the introductory Art. 1.9, and decimal point determination is a more important element here.

EXAMPLE 1.11A.   Calculate 250/495.

Solution: Set the hairline to 2.50 on D
Move the slide to place 4.95 on C beneath hairline
Read 5.05 on D opposite the right index

To place the decimal point using the single digit numbers

$$\frac{200}{500} = 0.4$$

Therefore, the answer is 0.505.   Or, using standard numbers:

$$\frac{250}{495} = \frac{\overset{+2}{2.50}}{\underset{+2}{4.95}} = \overset{0}{}$$

Although the resultant correction number is zero, since

$$2 - 2 = 0$$

the answer, 5.05, read from the slide rule, is not the correct decimal position. The ratio of the standard numbers is less than 1, and the zero correction number means that the answer must have zero correction to the decimal point position of

$$\frac{2}{5} = 0.4$$

Therefore, the answer is 0.505.

EXAMPLE 1.11B.   Calculate 6850/0.0842.

Solution: Set the hairline to 6.85 on D
Place 8.42 on C beneath the hairline
Read 8.14 on D opposite the right index

For placing the decimal point:

$$\frac{6850}{0.0842} = \frac{7000}{0.08} \text{ approx.} = \frac{7000}{0.10} \text{ approx.} = 70,000$$

Therefore, the answer is 81,400.

For purposes of placing the decimal point it is not necessary that the one digit of the given numbers be used. The mental arithmetic is sometimes simplified by rounding the numbers as in this example.

EXAMPLE 1.11C.   Calculate 0.0004215/34,200.

Solution: Set the hairline to 4.215 on D
Place 3.42 on C beneath the hairline
Read 1.232 on D opposite the right index of C

The standard number method of placing the decimal point is

$$\frac{0.0004215}{34,200} = \frac{\overset{-4}{4.215}}{\underset{+4}{3.42}} = \overset{-8}{1.232} = 0.00000001232$$

The usefulness of the standard number method is more evident in an extreme example of this nature. Probably the precision of the given numbers does not justify estimating the final digit, 2.

The following additional division examples omit the statement of slide rule manipulations, but show the manner of placing the decimal point.

EXAMPLE 1.11D.   Calculate 7.07/2600.

Solution:

$$\frac{7.07}{2600} = \frac{\overset{0}{7.07}}{\underset{+3}{2.600}} = \overset{-3}{2.72} = 0.00272$$

$$0 - (+3) = -3$$

EXAMPLE 1.11E.   Calculate 582/3.40.   *Solution:* Since 600/3 is 200, the answer is slightly less than 200, or is 171.

$$\frac{582}{3.40} = \frac{\overset{+2}{5.82}}{\underset{0}{3.40}} = \overset{+2}{1.71} = 171$$

EXAMPLE 1.11F. Calculate 1705/375. *Solution:* Since 1700/400 is slightly greater than 4, the answer is 4.55.

Although the foregoing examples refer to the C and D scales, any pair of mating logarithmic scales, one on the slide and one on the frame, may be used in the same manner for performing division. Thus, the A and B, or CF and DF scales of Fig. A.3., page 184, could be used for any of these examples and for the problems which follow. If CF and DF scales are used it should be noted that the index (or 1) is near the middle of the scale, not at the end as on C.

1.12. Numerical Problems in Division. For practical problems and examples on division applied to various fields of work, see Part II.

Additional numerical problems are given at the end of Chapter 1, including some in which only the decimal point is to be determined.

Perform the calculations indicated below.

	1F	1G	1H	1I	1J
a	$\dfrac{7}{4}$	$\dfrac{41}{25}$	$\dfrac{18}{13}$	$\dfrac{72}{17.4}$	$\dfrac{355}{11}$
b	$\dfrac{10}{2.08}$	$\dfrac{3.14}{90}$	$\dfrac{1816}{1976}$	$\dfrac{536}{2010}$	$\dfrac{715}{8323}$
c	$\dfrac{316}{574}$	$\dfrac{8760}{365}$	$\dfrac{0.7854}{6}$	$\dfrac{30.1}{747}$	$\dfrac{102}{427}$
d	$\dfrac{532}{1595}$	$\dfrac{195}{0.0137}$	$\dfrac{79.7}{3085}$	$\dfrac{0.28}{0.0136}$	$\dfrac{5225}{16.5}$
e	$\dfrac{0.2635}{0.00031}$	$\dfrac{233}{1027}$	$\dfrac{4.45}{0.01905}$	$\dfrac{268}{0.428}$	$\dfrac{0.387}{301}$
f	$\dfrac{1.595}{2135}$	$\dfrac{26.90}{0.277}$	$\dfrac{394}{0.0321}$	$\dfrac{0.554}{557}$	$\dfrac{30.8}{0.00275}$
g	$\dfrac{344}{0.1145}$	$\dfrac{0.0598}{0.2425}$	$\dfrac{0.466}{15.24}$	$\dfrac{28.2}{507}$	$\dfrac{1.89}{0.0393}$
h	$\dfrac{2.325}{67.25}$	$\dfrac{225.5}{4.575}$	$\dfrac{257.5}{0.33}$	$\dfrac{0.464}{354}$	$\dfrac{0.0764}{2.81}$
i	$\dfrac{8725}{1.663}$	$\dfrac{109.6}{0.1785}$	$\dfrac{4680}{54.3}$	$\dfrac{60.8}{0.0662}$	$\dfrac{0.2115}{0.001127}$
j	$\dfrac{23.21}{1.025}$	$\dfrac{467.2}{81.45}$	$\dfrac{900.5}{124.7}$	$\dfrac{8225}{26.4}$	$\dfrac{0.737}{0.00089}$
k	$\dfrac{305}{2.15}$	$\dfrac{0.517}{72.2}$	$\dfrac{4085}{24.05}$	$\dfrac{0.073}{320}$	$\dfrac{1515}{3.95}$
l	$\dfrac{2730}{1507}$	$\dfrac{2.77}{296}$	$\dfrac{529}{0.083}$	$\dfrac{7380}{4350}$	$\dfrac{0.920}{516}$

1.13. Multiplication of Two Numbers, C and D Scales. The basis for performing multiplication using the C and D scales is the addition of lengths proportional to the logarithms of the numbers, as described in Art. 1.3.

Logarithmic principle for multiplication:

If the logarithm of the first factor, M, *is added to the logarithm of the second factor,* N, *the sum is equal to the logarithm of the product,* P.

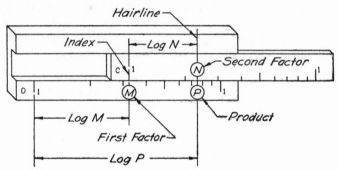

Fig. 1.17. Multiplication Principle

$\log M + \log N = \log P$; or $M \times N = P$

Consequently, the usual method, but not the only one, for operating the C and D scales of the slide rule to perform multiplication is:

Set the index of C to the first factor on D
Place the hairline over the second factor on C
Read the product on D beneath the hairline

EXAMPLE 1.13A. Calculate 5.5×1.5.

Solution: Set the left index of C to 5.5 on D
         Move the hairline to 1.5 on C
         Read 8.25 on D beneath the hairline
         See Fig. 1.18 for setting

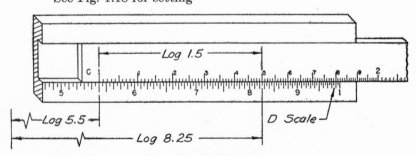

Fig. 1.18. Multiplication

Example 1.13A: $5.5 \times 1.5 = 8.25$

The sequence of terms in multiplication is immaterial.   The 1.5 could be set on D and the 5.5 on C.   There is a slight advantage in this latter sequence because the slide does not project out of the frame as far as in Fig. 1.18.   The importance of this is considered in Art. 1.16, on continued division and multiplication.

EXAMPLE 1.13B.   Calculate 5.5 × 2.   The first factor, 5.5, is one of the factors in the preceding example.   However, in Fig. 1.18 the 2 on C is observed to be beyond the end of the D scale graduations.   Because of the cyclic nature of the logarithmic scales, a change in setting to use the right index of C will bring the answer on scale.

Solution: Set the right index of C to 5.5 on D

　　　　 Move the hairline to 2 on C

　　　　 Read 1.1 (representing 11) on D beneath the hairline

EXAMPLE 1.13C.   Calculate 5.5 times each of the quantities 2.5, 3, 3.5, 4.   As noted in Example 1.12A, either factor in a product can be set on the D scale.   However, when one number is to be multiplied by several others it is better if the index of C is set to the common factor on D.   Moving the runner to the several quantities on C can be done faster than re-setting the slide several times.

Solution: Set the right index of C to 5.5 on D

　　　　 Move the hairline successively to 2.5, 3, 3.5, and 4 on D

　　　　 Read on D after placing the decimal point respectively 13.75, 16.5, 19.25, and 22

For these first examples of multiplication, the decimal point position has been readily apparent.   As in division, the similar simple number scheme or the standard number method may be used to place the decimal point.   It should be remembered that in multiplication the correction numbers of the factors are added algebraically, just as the lengths on the logarithmic scales are added.

The steps in applying the short-cut standard number method to multiplication are:

1. Write each factor as a standard number with the correction number above it.

2. Algebraically add the correction numbers of the factors and place this resultant correction number above the space for the answer.

3. Mentally approximate the product of the one-digit numbers and place the decimal point in the answer read from the slide rule in accordance with this mental approximation.

4. Express the standard number answer with its correction number in the usual form by moving the decimal point the number of places indicated by the resultant correction number.

EXAMPLE 1.13D.   Calculate 0.021 × 3200.

Solution: Set the left index of C to 2.1 on D
    Move the hairline to 3.2 on C
    Read 6.72 on D beneath the hairline

Applying the standard number method for placing the decimal point:

$$-2 \quad +3 \quad +1$$
$$0.021 \times 3200 = 2.1 \times 3.2 = 6.72 = 67.2$$

The resultant correction number is

$$-2 + 3 = +1$$

and the mental approximation for the one-digit standard numbers is

$$2 \times 3 = 6$$

Therefore, the answer is 67.2.

EXAMPLE 1.13E.   Calculate 810 × 0.83.

Solution: Set the right index of C to 8.1 on D
    Move the hairline to 8.3 on C
    Read 6.72 on D beneath the hairline

For placing the decimal point:

$$+2 \quad -1 \quad +1$$
$$810 \times 0.83 = 8.1 \times 8.3 = 67.2 = 672$$

The mental approximation for the one-digit numbers is

$$8 \times 8 = 64$$

not 6, as it is in the preceding example.

Although the resultant correction numbers are the same and the digits of the answer as read on the slide rule are the same in these two examples, the latter is 10 times as much as the former.   The mental arithmetic with the standard numbers is seen as a necessary step in placing the decimal point correctly.

The standard number method is illustrated in this example for purposes of comparison with the preceding one.   However, the similar simple number scheme is probably more satisfactory in this case, giving

$$800 \times 0.8 = 640$$

EXAMPLE 1.13F.   Calculate 0.000562 × 172.   In a problem such as Example 1.13E, in which both numbers are near the right end of the scale, it is easy to recognize that the right-hand index of C must be used to bring the answer on the scale.   In the present example, trial is the only guide.

In the discussion of Example 1.13A it is suggested that the best sequence of factors is one which will require the slide to project from the frame the least.   Therefore, in this example if one attempts to use the right-hand index of C, it should be set to the factor 5.62; if the left-hand index is tried it should be set to 1.72.   Since it is the left index which must be used, the solution is:

Set the left index of C to 1.72 on D
Move the hairline to 5.62 on C
Read 9.66 on D beneath the hairline

For placing the decimal point

$$0.000562 \times 172 \overset{-4}{=} 5.62 \times 1.72 \overset{+2}{=} 9.66 \overset{-2}{=} 0.0966$$

In performing the mental arithmetic, the one-digit numbers

$$5 \times 1 = 5$$

will give correct decimal point location.   As another plan rounding off to the nearest one-digit numbers would give

$$6 \times 2 = 12$$

Since this plan of rounding off increases both factors above the given values, 6×2 is obviously greater than 5.62×1.72, and the correct value is less than 12, and therefore the decimal point belongs after the 9. However, a plan which gives a closer check on errors is to round off one factor in a product to the next larger one-digit number and to use the next smaller one-digit number for the other factor.   Thus,

$$5 \times 2 = 10$$

gives a closer approximation of 9.66 than the other one-digit combinations suggested.

The following additional multiplication examples omit the statement of slide rule manipulations, but show the manner of determining the decimal point position.

EXAMPLE 1.13G.   Calculate 0.0731×6500.   Rounding the numbers:

$$0.07 \times 7000 = 490$$

Therefore, the answer is 475.   Or, using a standard number notation:

$$0.0731 \times 6500 \overset{-2}{=} 7.31 \times 6.50 \overset{+3}{=} 47.5 \overset{+1}{=} 475$$

EXAMPLE 1.13H.   Calculate 1590×185.   Rounding the numbers:

$$1500 \times 200 = 300{,}000$$

Therefore, the answer is 294,000. Using the standard number form:

$$\overset{+3}{1590} \times \overset{+2}{185} = 1.59 \times 1.85 = \overset{+5}{2.94} = 294,000$$

1.14. Numerical Problems in Multiplication. For practical problems and examples in multiplication applied to various fields of work, see Part II.

Additional numerical problems are given at the end of Chapter 1, including some in which only the decimal point is to be determined.

	1K	1L	1M	1N
a	1.01 × 5.05	1.24 × 7.5	1.07 × 5.8	1.005 × 36.5
b	1.23 × 83	1.3 × 57	0.25 × 290	8.1 × 24.8
c	438 × 2.08	0.000812 × 7700	0.024 × 126	1.095 × 0.0762
d	182 × 44.3	927 × 0.307	47.5 × 0.0113	3850 × 265
e	0.0236 × 4.13	84.7 × 365	18.75 × 40.3	2975 × 0.0037
f	19 × 27	5.02 × 155	262 × 115	37.9 × 552
g	62 × 4.35	0.31 × 87.2	0.41 × 0.032	655 × 0.0061
h	1.925 × 0.134	57.3 × 0.0732	22.2 × 61.5	98.3 × 75.5
i	7.07 × 143	31.9 × 6.55	522 × 408	16.7 × 27.8
j	0.0557 × 2.11	6030 × 324	888 × 192	23.4 × 56.7
k	30.6 × 9.19	2.46 × 188	455 × 630	75 × 368
1	0.474 × 16.4	28.1 × 147	0.00136 × 714	92 × 0.0863
m	0.0809 × 0.051	0.0041 × 0.378	84.8 × 75.2	606 × 166
n	19.85 × 0.455	837 × 375	0.0346 × 0.029	98.2 × 32.9
o	5280 × 471	1.035 × 90.9	26.2 × 11.52	3030 × 0.00171
p	0.000237 × 0.029	17.28 × 1440	52.1 × 62.3	46.0 × 416
q	1370 × 2860	407 × 2.16	64.2 × 118	0.027 × 1930
r	275 × 0.182	727 × 77.2	12.3 × 0.137	5470 × 486
s	0.084 × 0.091	0.428 × 0.0262	52.4 × 47.2	1760 × 212
t	7.15 × 18.6	67.8 × 0.00226	0.386 × 6.16	1.072 × 5.95

1.15. Meaning of Accuracy; Increasing the Accuracy of Computation. Many practical computation problems, including the representative group presented in Part II, involve numerical operations about physical things or physical properties. It is characteristic of all measurement (except counting a number of objects) that approximation is necessary in the process. This is true whether the measurement is length, angle, volume, weight, time interval, electrical properties, or other phenomena.

The instruments of measurement are similar to the slide rule in that they possess a graduated scale. The graduated scale often is not logarithmic, but it is graphic, whether on a protractor, scale, clock, or voltmeter.

It is obvious that calculations made with approximate data are themselves approximations. The degree of approximation is occasionally a matter of some concern. Therefore some definitions on accuracy of measurement and of calculations with measured data require more careful consideration.

Several terms used to describe accuracy of numerical quantities are: significant figures, per cent error, and probable error. As an example, if the diameter of the earth is known to be greater than 7.5 thousand miles and less than 8.5 thousand miles, the value, correct to one significant figure, is 8 thousand miles. If it is known as lying between 78.5 hundred and 79.5 hundred miles, it may be said that the diameter, correct to two significant figures, is 79 hundred miles. If this example is carried to one more significant figure, it is necessary to restrict the definition of diameter, since the earth is not a geometric sphere. The equatorial diameter is 793×10 miles, meaning that the value is nearer to 7930 than to 7920 or 7940. The per cent errors corresponding to these expressions are:

$$\frac{0.5}{8} \times 100 \text{ or less, } \frac{0.5}{79} \times 100 \text{ or less, and } \frac{0.5}{793.0} \times 100 \text{ or less}$$

These reduce to 6 per cent, 0.63 per cent, and 0.0630 per cent. These percentages are expressed with one, two, and three significant figures, respectively, corresponding to the number of significant figures in the several diameters.

From statistical studies it is known that the error of measuring the equatorial diameter is probably less than 330 feet, or 0.062 miles and the most probable value is 7926.69 miles, although it cannot be known with certainty that the diameter is not several hundred feet, or perhaps a thousand feet larger or smaller. Most likely it is less than 330 feet away from the probable value. This amount is called the probable error of measurement of equatorial diameter.

The accuracy of the C and D scales of the slide rule may be considered in a similar manner. If an error of one graduation interval is made in reading the scale so that 1.01 is read for a calculation in which the exact value is 1.00, the result is correct to two significant figures (the third digit being in doubt), and the error is 1.0 per cent. If 1.99 is read in place of 2.00, the result is again correct to two significant figures, but the error is only 1 in 200, or 0.5 per cent. At numbers just greater than 4 on the 10-inch C and D scales an error of one graduation interval is 1.2 per cent. For any other portion of the scales, an error of one graduation interval lies between 0.50 and 1.2 per cent.

In reading the slide rule, an error of one graduation interval is large; it is possible to estimate proportional distances between graduations quite accurately. It has been found from many computations that the probable error of reading the C and D scales of a 10-inch slide rule is about one-twentieth of one per cent. The probable error of computation increases with the number of factors in the problem and the number of readings and settings on the scales.

The accuracy of the given data and the use to be made of the answer determine whether a slide rule is sufficiently accurate. If the numerical data for a problem are correct to three significant figures, any computations made with the data will not be correct to more than three significant figures. For many of the applications of Part II, the methods for obtaining the data, and consequently the data, are correct to no more than three significant figures. Even when data are correct to more than three significant figures, the purpose of the computations may make a slide rule entirely satisfactory.

Although accuracy of data and accuracy of computations are not elements of the simple numerical problems of Part I, it is helpful to examine the nature of slide rule accuracy along with the study of division and multiplication. Also, it is desirable to consider a method for securing results more accurate than can be read directly from the slide rule.

By splitting a factor into two, or sometimes three, parts, and performing part of the numerical operation with slide rule and part of it mentally or with pencil and paper, it is possible to obtain one more significant figure in multiplication or division with very little additional labor. The following numerical examples illustrate more clearly than words the method for doing this and at the same time show how to keep the mental arithmetic simple.

EXAMPLE 1.15A.

$$\frac{6770}{5900} = \frac{5900 + 870}{5900} = \frac{5900}{5900_m} + \frac{870}{5900_s} = 1 + 0.1475$$

The subscript, m, identifies the operation done by mental arithmetic; s identifies the slide rule operation.

EXAMPLE 1.15B.

$$\frac{16,875}{14.26} = \frac{14,260 + 2615}{14.26} = \frac{14,260}{14.26_m} + \frac{2615}{14.26_s} = 1000 + 183.5$$

EXAMPLE 1.15C.

$$\frac{5280}{125} = \frac{5000 + 280}{125} = \frac{5000}{125_s} + \frac{280}{125_s} = 40 + 2.240$$

The number 5000 is selected for one part because 5000/125 is a simple integer, and may in this example be computed with the slide rule.

EXAMPLE 1.15D.

$$\frac{0.09207}{1625} = \frac{(0.00005 \times 1625) + ?}{1625} = \frac{0.08125 + 0.01082}{1625}$$

EXAMPLE 1.15E.

$$\frac{1216}{627} = \frac{1254 - 38}{627} = \frac{1254}{627_m} - \frac{38}{627_s} = 2 - 0.0606$$

EXAMPLE 1.15F.

$$1.269 \times 4875 = 1.269(5000 - 125) = 6345 - 158.6$$

EXAMPLE 1.15G.

$$2.516 \times 5.287 = 2.516(5 + 0.287)$$

Multiplication by 5 is the same as multiplication by 10/2; this is an easy operation mentally since moving the decimal point one place multiplies by 10. Mental division by 2 is readily performed.

1.16. Continued Division and Multiplication, C and D Scales. The ratio of two numbers or the product of two numbers, Arts. 1.11 and 1.13, are slide rule calculations very frequently encountered. However, many other practical calculation problems result in quantities like:

$$\frac{95 \times 42 \times 81 \times 12}{75 \times 31 \times 19}$$

The first thought in attacking a problem of this nature is to perform the numerator products, then the denominator products, and finally the division of the two. This method is workable, but not as satisfactory for slide rule solution with C and D scales as alternate division and multiplication. Using this latter procedure only the final answer need be read, thus avoiding some of the inaccuracy of estimating intermediate scale readings. Also, the suggested method is faster because it requires fewer settings of the slide.

Several examples are presented which illustrate typical problems and difficulties associated with continued division and multiplication. It is desirable for the reader to make the settings with a slide rule as he follows the description with the examples.

EXAMPLE 1.16A.   Calculate $30 \times 6/9$

Solution: Set the hairline to 3 on D
Set 9 on C beneath the hairline
To multiply by 6, move the hairline to 6 on C
Read 2 on D beneath the hairline

The result of the division, 30/9, may be read following the second step by reading opposite the right index of C, but it is not necessary to read it. The decimal point position, 20, is easily found in this case. See Fig. 1.19 for the setting.

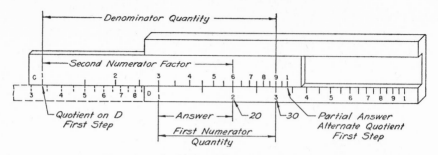

Fig. 1.19.   Continued Division and Multiplication

Example 1.16A: $30 \times 6/9 = 20$; or $\log 30 - \log 9 + \log 6 = \log 20$

EXAMPLE 1.16B.   Calculate $75 \times 18/13$.

Solution: Set the hairline to 7.5 on D
Set 1.3 on C beneath the hairline

The result of this division appears on D opposite the index of C.   To multiply by 18, the hairline might be moved to 1.8 on C; however, Fig. 1.20 shows 1.8 to be beyond the end of D.   It is shown in Example 1.13B

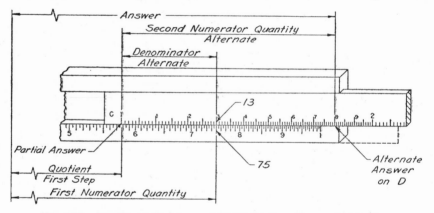

Fig. 1.20.   Continued Division and Multiplication: Reversal of Indices

Example 1.16B: $75 \times 18/13 = 104$ Operation: Place hairline to partial answer, 75/13, while reversing indices to multiply by 18

that when one factor in a product appears off the scale, changing to the other index of C will bring the product on scale.   The hairline may be used to hold a partial answer while changing indices.   Thus, the succeeding steps are:

Move the hairline to the left index of C
Set the right index of C beneath the hairline
Move the hairline to 1.8 on C
Read 1.04 (to three significant figures) on D beneath the hairline

To place the decimal point it may be noted that 18/13 is approximately one and one-third; and 75 times one and one-third is 100. Therefore, the answer is 104.

Folded scales, described in Art. 1.20, may be used to avoid the need for reversing indices in problems like this, thus eliminating one setting of the slide.

EXAMPLE 1.16C. Calculate $\dfrac{13.75 \times 468}{0.00216}$. This example is similar to Example 1.16A in slide rule setting. The reader may verify that the significant figures of the answer are 2.98. Placing the decimal point is more difficult than for the preceding example, and this is a good example on which to use the standard number method.

As an obvious extension of the method described in Art. 1.10, the resultant correction number for continued division and multiplication equals the algebraic sum of numerator correction numbers minus the algebraic sum of denominator correction numbers. Thus

$$\frac{13.75 \times 468}{0.00216} = \frac{\overset{+1}{1.375} \times \overset{+2}{4.68}}{\underset{-3}{2.16}}$$

and

$$(+1 + 2) - (-3) = +6$$

for the one-digit numbers

$$\frac{1 \times 5}{2} = 2.5$$

$$\overset{+6}{}$$

Therefore, the answer is 2.98, or 2,980,000. As noted in Art. 1.10, this is merely a short-hand way for writing

$$\frac{1.375 \times 10^1 \times 4.68 \times 10^2}{2.16 \times 10^{-3}} = \frac{1.375 \times 4.68}{2.16} \times \frac{10^1 \times 10^2}{10^{-3}}$$

EXAMPLE 1.16D. Calculate $\dfrac{42.5 \times 871}{0.00124}$. This example requires a reversal of the slide to use the alternate index of C for the final multiplication. The significant figures of the answer are again 2.98. To place the decimal point

$$\frac{42.5 \times 871}{0.00124} = \frac{\overset{+1}{4.25} \times \overset{+2}{8.71}}{\underset{-3}{1.24}}$$

and
$$(+1 +2) - (-3) = +6$$

For the one-digit numbers
$$\frac{4 \times 8}{1} = 32$$
$$+6$$

Therefore, the answer is 29.8, or 29,800,000. A comparison with Example 1.16C shows that the resultant correction number is the same, and the digits of the answer are the same. However, the decimal point position for the one-digit numbers is different, and thus the answer is 10 times as large for Example 1.16D as for 1.16C.

EXAMPLE 1.16E. Calculate $\dfrac{0.526 \times 746}{29.2 \times 9.15}$. If division by 29.2 is attempted first, it will be found that a reversal of indices and thus an extra setting of the slide is necessary. If the slide rule has folded scales, the method described in Art. 1.20 will avoid the extra setting. However, the extra setting can be avoided using C and D scales only if division by 9.15 is carried out first.

It makes no difference in this problem whether 0.526/9.15 or 745/9.15 is performed first. However, as a general procedure, if 746/9.15 is performed first, the greater portion of the C scale will be within the frame and in position for subsequent multiplication by a greater range of numbers without reversing indices.

Solution: Divide 7.46 by 9.15
    Multiply the result by 5.26
    Divide this result by 2.92
    Read 1.47 on D opposite the left index of C

If the terms are rearranged in the order of the operations
$$\frac{7.46}{9.15} \quad \frac{5.26}{2.92}$$

Or, writing the procedure as a logarithmic equation
$$\log 7.46_D - \log 9.15_C + \log 5.26_D - \log 2.92_C = \log 1.47_D$$

The subscripts, D and C, indicate the scales on which the numbers are set. The decimal point may be placed by observing that
$$\frac{0.5 \times 800}{30 \times 9} = \frac{400}{270}$$

is a little greater than 1. Or, using the standard number method
$$\frac{0.526 \times 746}{29.2 \times 9.15} = \frac{\overset{-1}{5.26} \times \overset{+2}{7.46}}{\underset{+1}{2.92} \times \underset{0}{9.15}}$$

and
$$(-1 +2) - (+1 +0) = 0$$

The one-digit numbers give
$$\frac{5 \times 7}{3 \times 9} = \frac{35}{27} = 1+$$

Therefore, the answer is 1.47.

EXAMPLE 1.16F.   Calculate $\dfrac{909 \times 0.515 \times 0.00324}{245 \times 0.782}$.   This is also an example in which reversal of indices is necessary if 909/245 is performed first.   Any other division sequence may be used and reversal of indices will be avoided.   The recommended sequence, which keeps the slide most nearly centered in the frame, is

$$
\begin{array}{ccc}
+2 & -3 & -1 \\
9.09 & 3.24 & 5.15 \\
\hline
7.82 & 2.45 & \\
-1 & +2 &
\end{array}
$$

The resultant correction number is
$$(+2 - 3 - 1) - (-1 + 2) = -3$$

The one-digit numbers reduce to
$$\frac{9 \times 3 \times 5}{8 \times 2} = \frac{9 \times 15}{16} = 9-$$
$$-3$$

Therefore, the answer is 7.91, or 0.00791.

It is not necessary to rewrite the numbers in the sequence in which they are set on the slide rule, as has been done here.   It is desirable in a long series of calculations to place a check mark near each quantity as it is set on the slide rule.   This is a protection against duplication of some term, particularly if the sequence of setting is different from the given sequence.

EXAMPLE 1.16G.   Calculate 0.0142 × 792 × 16.5.   It is possible to multiply three quantities with one setting of the slide by using the CI scale along with C and D.   The method is described in Art. 1.18.   Not all slide rules have a CI scale, and in any case, mastery of C and D scales is desirable before taking up other scales.   The solution presented here used C and D scales only.

Solution: The sequence of operations is immaterial.   However, multiplication of 7.92 by 1.42 keeps the slide more nearly centered in the frame; then the result of this product is the first factor in a product with 1.65. The steps in the operation are:

Set the right index of C to 7.92 on D
Move the hairline to 1.42 on C

Set the left index of C to the hairline
Move the hairline to 1.65 on C
Read 1.855 on D beneath the hairline

For placing the decimal point

$$\overset{-2}{0.0142} \times \overset{+2}{792} \times \overset{+1}{16.5} = 1.42 \times 7.92 \times 1.65$$

The resultant correction number is

$$-2 + 2 + 1 = +1$$

and for the one-digit numbers

$$1 \times 8 \times 2 = 16$$

$$\overset{+1}{}$$

Therefore, the answer is 18.55, or 185.5.

EXAMPLE 1.16H. Calculate $\dfrac{5650}{275 \times 22.2}$. *Solution:* There is one less numerator quantity than denominator quantity. Again, by using the CI scale with C and D the minimum motion of the slide results. Using the C and D scales only, it is a good plan to factor out a 1 and perform the sequence of operations shown diagrammatically

$$\frac{D}{C}\ \frac{1}{22.2}\ \frac{5650}{275}$$

The significant figures of the answer are 9.26. To place the decimal point similar simple numbers show

$$\frac{6000}{20 \times 300} = \frac{6000}{6000} = 1$$

Therefore, the answer is 0.926.

EXAMPLE 1.16I. Calculate $\dfrac{1}{388 \times 522}$. The slide remains more nearly centered in the frame if 1/5.22 is performed first selecting the 1 at the right end of D. The suggested solution is:

Set 5.22 on C to the right index of D
Move the hairline to the left index of C
Place 3.88 on C beneath the hairline
Read 4.94 on D at the right index of C

To place the decimal point

$$\frac{1}{388 \times 522} = \underset{+2\quad +2}{\frac{1}{3.88 \times 5.22}} = \overset{-4}{0.0494} = 0.00000494$$

since the resultant correction number is

$$0 - (+2 +2) = -4$$

and for the one-digit numbers

$$\frac{1}{4 \times 5} = \frac{1}{20} = 0.05$$

EXAMPLE 1.16J.   Determine U in the proportion: $\dfrac{2.5}{3.2} = \dfrac{6.8}{U}$.   One method is to solve for U, obtaining

$$U = \frac{3.2 \times 6.8}{2.5}$$

However, in the given form it may be observed that the ratio, 2.5/3.2, equals the ratio, 6.8/U, or in logarithmic form

$$\log 2.5_\mathrm{D} - \log 3.2_\mathrm{C} = \log 6.8_\mathrm{D} - \log U_\mathrm{C}$$

The subscripts, D and C, indicate the scales on which the numbers are set.   In other words, the solution is:

  Set 3.2 on C to 2.5 on D
  At 6.8 on D read U equals 8.7 on C

This method is especially useful if there is a continued proportion, such as

$$\frac{2.5}{3.2} = \frac{6.8}{U} = \frac{V}{4.4} = \frac{15}{Y}$$

Fig. 1.21 illustrates the principle of solution for a continued proportion. The numerator quantities are then all on the D scale, matched with

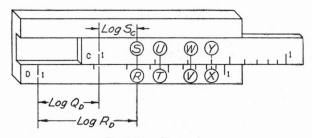

Fig. 1.21.   Proportion

$$\frac{R}{S} = \frac{T}{U} = \frac{V}{W} = \frac{X}{Y} = Q$$

$$\log Q_\mathrm{D} = \log R_\mathrm{D} - \log S_\mathrm{C} = \log T_\mathrm{D} - \log U_\mathrm{C}$$
$$= \log V_\mathrm{D} - \log W_\mathrm{C} = \log X_\mathrm{D} - \log Y_\mathrm{C}$$

corresponding denominator quantities on C. V may be read as 3.44, and Y is 19.2.

It would be equally satisfactory, and sometimes desirable, to invert and set all numerator terms on the C scale with the corresponding denominator terms on the D scale.

1.17. Numerical Problems in Continued Division and Multiplication. For practical problems and examples applied to various fields or work, see Part II.

Additional numerical problems are given at the end of Chapter 1, including some in which only the decimal point is to be determined. Calculate the following.

	1P	1Q	1R
a	$\dfrac{1.35 \times 23.75}{10.8 \times 0.0356 \times 67.3}$	$\dfrac{1.04 \times 9.32 \times 57.6}{1853 \times 0.0855}$	$\dfrac{6.35 \times 43.5}{92.1}$
b	$\dfrac{938 \times 456}{1355 \times 0.0242 \times 17.35}$	$\dfrac{364 \times 1.05 \times 793}{1.95 \times 809}$	$\dfrac{1530 \times 9080}{16,800}$
c	$\dfrac{6.24 \times 128.5}{41.75 \times 3.75 \times 9.55}$	$\dfrac{0.132 \times 0.045 \times 1352}{0.576 \times 435}$	$\dfrac{1}{39}$
d	$\dfrac{0.585 \times 0.0734}{0.00248 \times 10.76 \times 0.158}$	$\dfrac{39.3 \times 715 \times 1436}{5195 \times 3480}$	$\dfrac{1}{4567}$
e	$\dfrac{0.0325 \times 0.00959 \times 0.165}{0.0246}$	$\dfrac{9.43 \times 2.16 \times 53.2}{105.8}$	$\dfrac{7.1 \times 323}{2150}$
f	$\dfrac{48.5 \times 0.284}{136.5 \times 0.00473 \times 16.82}$	$\dfrac{0.532 \times 373 \times 778}{12.580}$	$\dfrac{1}{0.835}$
g	$\dfrac{10,080 \times 92.5 \times 0.0375}{186.5}$	$\dfrac{1.82 \times 4.56 \times 932}{1652}$	$\dfrac{0.265 \times 0.632}{0.0842}$
h	$\dfrac{0.00184 \times 1362 \times 254}{81.5}$	$\dfrac{1635 \times 216 \times 104}{10,400 \times 545}$	$\dfrac{93 \times 42 \times 67}{103 \times 0.912}$
i	$\dfrac{0.73 \times 0.0109 \times 0.742}{0.0648}$	$\dfrac{746 \times 235 \times 1570}{916 \times 425}$	$\dfrac{5070 \times 1830}{41,800}$
j	$\dfrac{22,790 \times 550 \times 0.725}{33,000 \times 957}$	$\dfrac{13,846 \times 2080}{54.5 \times 7.82 \times 238}$	$\dfrac{3190 \times 0.0375}{0.2725}$
k	$\dfrac{1.97 \times 2.06 \times 0.0107}{0.0034 \times 9.63}$	$\dfrac{4275 \times 1.755}{31,600}$	$\dfrac{0.905 \times 0.0035}{0.01720}$
l	$\dfrac{4.53 \times 10.75 \times 0.83}{0.312 \times 104}$	$\dfrac{1}{0.00734}$	$\dfrac{653 \times 345}{70,500}$
m	$\dfrac{35 \times 1.325 \times 0.515}{10.3 \times 0.872}$	$\dfrac{1}{7.85}$	$\dfrac{3175 \times 234}{5760}$
n	$\dfrac{2.14 \times 12.2 \times 2.36}{8.45 \times 6.36}$	$\dfrac{0,912 \times 0.0464}{0.0786}$	$\dfrac{1}{19,750}$
o	$71,500 \times 0.00435 \times 135$	$1.675 \times 249 \times 8925$	$358 \times 1.655 \times 5.05$
p	$7890 \times 0.00535 \times 805$	$1090 \times 53,800 \times 7350$	$43 \times 976 \times 0.053$

1.18. The Inverted Scale. The CI, or C Inverted, scale found on many slide rules is a logarithmic scale increasing in the opposite direction from the C and D scales; or, it is a negative logarithmic scale. Some slide rules have been made with an inverted B scale. Of course inversion of any one of the usual scales is possible. The negative logarithm property of the CI scale makes it useful for several purposes, one being to find reciprocals of numbers.

If the hairline is set to a number on the C scale, the reciprocal (except for decimal point) may be read on the CI scale.

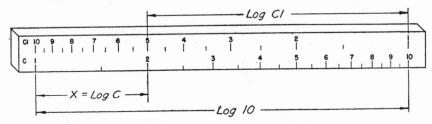

Fig. 1.22. The CI Scale Principle

In terms of logarithmic equations and the general diagram, Fig. 1.22, it is evident that

$$x = \log C = \log 10 - \log C_I = \log \frac{10}{C_I}$$

or

$$C = \frac{10}{C_I}$$

Ignoring the decimal point

$$C = \frac{1}{C_I}$$

On the preceding pages, settings and readings on the slide rule are referred to by standard number, since one cycle only (1 to 10) of the logarithmic scale represents all numbers. Thus, the slide rule setting for the numbers 185, 18.5, or 0.0185 has been referred to as 1.85. On this and subsequent pages this distinction is dropped for most discussions. Reference to a setting of 18.5 or 0.0185 is understood to mean 1.85 on the one cycle logarithmic scale.

EXAMPLE 1.18A. Find reciprocals for (a) 15, (b) 21, (c) 2.44, (d) 0.0362, (e) 37.6, (f) 0.49, (g) 5.79, (h) 68.9, (i) 833, (j) 0.952.

Solution: Set the hairline successively to 15, 21, etc. on C
Read on CI beneath the hairline; (a) 0.0667, (b) 0.0476, (c) 0.410, (d) 27.6, (e) 0.0266, (f) 2.04, (g) 0.1727, (h) 0.0145, (i) 0.00120, (j) 1.05

Fig. 1.23 illustrates a few of these examples. Referring to Figs. A.1 through A.8, pages 182–189, it will be observed that the CI scales may be at the edge of the slide or away from the edge. Fig. 1.23 shows it away from the edge, and omits other scales not used.

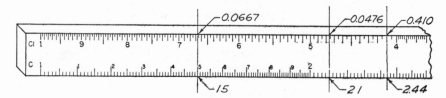

Fig. 1.23. Reciprocals on C and CI Scales

Example 1.18A: $1/15 = 0.0667$; $1/21 = 0.0476$; $1/2.44 = 0.410$

One may, with equal ease, set on the CI scale and read the reciprocals on the C scale.

Some duplex slide rules do not have the C and CI scales on the same side. Since the D scale is just like the C scale except for being on the frame, it is possible to find reciprocals by aligning the CI scale with the D scale and then use them in the same manner as the C and CI scales in Example 1.18A.

In like manner, CF and CIF scales, D and DI scales, or any other pair of matching direct and inverted logarithmic scales may be used to find reciprocals. The necessary condition is that the indices on the direct scale match those on the inverted scale. Consequently, it is also possible to read reciprocals by using, on a slide rule having such scales, CF with DI, D with CIF, by merely matching indices.

If one has a slide rule which does not include a CI scale, the equivalent of a CI scale may be obtained by withdrawing the slide and inserting it reversed. Reciprocals can be read using D with the reversed C scale, Fig. 1.24.

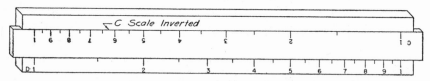

Fig. 1.24. Reversed C Scale for CI: Partially Graduated Scale

Because the inverted scale is in effect a negative logarithmic scale, it may be manipulated in a manner common for division, that is, for a subtraction of logarithms, and yet accomplish a multiplication or addition of logarithms. Thus, by using the CI and D scales for multiplication of two numbers there is no difficulty with one factor falling off the scale and having to reverse indices to bring it on scale.

The procedure for operating CI and D scales to perform multiplication is:

Set the hairline to the first factor, *M*, on D
Move the slide to place the second factor, *N*, on CI beneath the hairline
Read the product, *P*, on D opposite the index
See the diagram, Fig. 1.25

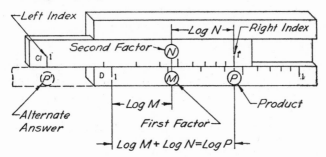

Fig. 1.25. **Multiplication Principle: CI and D Scales**

$\log M + \log N = \log P$; or $M \times N = P$

EXAMPLE 1.18B.   Calculate 1.3×8 using CI and D scales.

Solution: Set the hairline to 1.3 on D
Place 8 on CI beneath the hairline
Read 10.4 on D opposite the index of CI
See Fig. 1.26

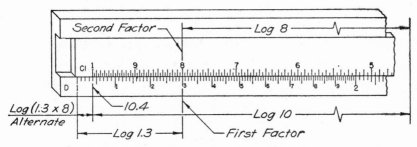

Fig. 1.26. **Multiplication: CI and D Scales**
(Example 1.18B: $1.3 \times 8 = 10.4$)

Any pair of logarithmic scales which may be used for performing multiplication may also be used for division by changing the method of operation. Thus, division may also be performed using CI and D scales. For performing a single division, the method has no superiority over the use of C and D scales. For a series of divisions with the same numerator, one of the common factor problems of Art. 1.19, the method is very useful.

The procedure for operation of CI and D scales to perform division is:

Set the index of CI to the numerator on D
Move the hairline to the denominator on CI
Read the quotient on D beneath the hairline

EXAMPLE 1.18C. Calculate 12/8 using CI and D scales.

Solution: Set the left index of CI to 12 on D
Move the hairline to 8 on CI
Read 1.5 on D beneath the hairline

Using C, D, and CI scales it is possible to multiply three factors with one setting of the slide. This is generally faster than using two slide settings as required if only C and D scales are used. However, reversal of indices is sometimes necessary, which is no faster than using C and D alone.

EXAMPLE 1.18D. Calculate $2 \times 8 \times 1.1$ using C, D, and CI scales.

Solution: Set 8 on CI to 2 on D
Move the hairline to 1.1 on C
Read 17.6 on D beneath the hairline

The intermediate product, 8×2, may be read opposite the index of CI. Fig. 1.27 shows the setting.

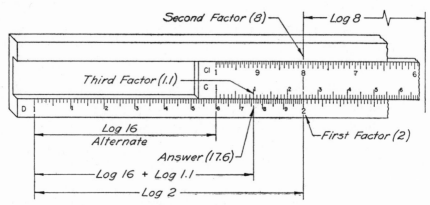

Fig. 1.27. Three Factor Multiplication: D, CI, and C Scales
Example 1.18D: $2 \times 8 \times 1.1 = 17.6$

EXAMPLE 1.18E. Calculate $2 \times 8 \times 0.7$.

Solution: Set 2 on CI to 8 on D
Move the hairline to the left index of CI
Move the slide to put the right index of C at the hairline
Set the hairline to 0.7 on C
Read 11.2 on D beneath the hairline

Reversal of indices is necessary for the last product, since 0.7 on the C scale is beyond the end of D.   Changing the sequence of factors will not help in this example.   It can be solved, however, with one slide setting on a slide rule with folded scales, Art. 1.20.

EXAMPLE 1.18F.   Calculate 14 × 9.25 × 605.

Solution: Set the hairline to 605 on D
　　　　　Place 14 on CI beneath the hairline
　　　　　At 9.25 on C read 78,300 on D

The choice of scale on which to set each of the factors is arbitrary.   The setting described leads to the minimum movement of slide and runner from the center.

EXAMPLE 1.18G.   Solve for *U*, *V*, and *W* in the continued equation:
3.27 × 5.30 = 4.0 × *U* = 7.1 × *V* = 8.25 × *W*

Solution: Set the hairline to 5.30 on D
　　　　　Place 3.27 on CI beneath the hairline
　　　　　At 4.0 on CI read *U* equals 4.33 on D
　　　　　At 7.1 on CI read *V* equals 2.44 on D
　　　　　At 8.25 on CI read *W* equals 2.10 on D

The product of each of these pairs of numbers appears on D at the index of CI.   Any hairline position will indicate on the CI and D scales a pair of numbers whose product is the same.

EXAMPLE 1.18H.   Calculate $\dfrac{1}{2.30 \times 0.935}$.

Solution: Set the hairline to 2.30 on D
　　　　　Set 0.935 on CI beneath the hairline
　　　　　Read the answer, 0.465, on C at the right index of D

The product of the denominator factors would appear on D opposite the index of CI (or C); its reciprocal appears on C opposite the index of D.

EXAMPLE 1.18I.   Calculate $\dfrac{1}{3.98 \times 4.6 \times 2.8}$.

Solution: Set the hairline to 3.98 on D
　　　　　Place 4.6 on CI beneath the hairline
　　　　　At 2.8 on C read 0.0195 on DI

If the slide rule does not have a DI scale it would be necessary to obtain the reciprocal of the triple product by an additional operation.

In the day to day operation of the slide rule, efforts to use the very minimum number of settings to obtain the answer may not be worth while.   If one has a series of calculations, similar in form, a few minutes spent in finding the shortest method of computation are worth while.

Certain of the foregoing examples using inverted scales show the possi-bilities for obtaining solutions with minimum settings. To develop facility in selecting the shortest method requires considerable practice.

1.19. Common Factors in Division and Multiplication. A simple and frequently occurring common factor problem is in the determination of percentage composition. An introductory example is presented to illus-trate the nature of the problem.

EXAMPLE 1.19A. Given components of 5.2, 17.3, 4.7, and 26.4; what percentage is each of the total? Common factor problems, contrary to this example, are often met in the form of a table. Even when not tabular it is usually desirable to set the given data down in a table, with blank spaces for the calculation results.

Given Data	5.2	17.3	4.7	26.4	53.6 Total
Required					100.0% Total

The percentages are: $100 \times 5.2/53.6$, $100 \times 17.3/53.6$, $100 \times 4.7/53.6$, $100 \times 26.4/53.6$. The ratio, $100/53.6$, is a common term in all of the percentages. Therefore, by solving the common term first, the successive percentages may be obtained with one setting of the slide.

Solution: Set 53.6 on C to the right index (100) on D
　　　　Move the hairline successively to the given values on C, 5.2, 17.3, 4.7, 26.4
　　　　Read the products on D beneath the hairline

The table then is

Given Data	5.2	17.3	4.7	26.4	53.6 Total
Required	9.7	32.3	8.8	49.2	100.0 Total
Alternate	10	32	9	49	100 Total

If values to the nearest per cent only are desired, the values read from the slide rule may be rounded as shown in the "Alternate" row.

EXAMPLE 1.19B. Calculate percentages for the following:

Given	12.5	6.3	5.3	21.9	46.0 Total
Percentages					

In Example 1.19A all of the percentages can be completed without reversal of indices. For Example 1.19B, reversal of indices is necessary if C and D scales are used. It is faster if all calculations with one setting are completed before reversing indices.

Solution: Set 46 on C to the right index of D
　　　　At 12.5 on C read 27.2 on D
　　　　At 21.9 on C read 47.6 on D

Reversing indices

> Set 46 on C to the left index of D
> At 6.3 on C read 13.7 on D
> At 5.3 on C read 11.5 on D

If one has a slide rule with folded scales, reversal of indices as described here is not necessary. See Art. 1.20.

EXAMPLE 1.19C. Calculate percentages for the following: 42.0, 15.2, 4.2, 48.6, 42.0, which total 152.0. Two slide rule settings only are needed for the 5 percentages.

Characteristic of the foregoing examples is the occurrence of the same denominator with several different numerators. If, instead, one numerator is common for several different denominators, the calculations can be completed with one setting, or sometimes two settings, of the slide by using the CI and D scales.

EXAMPLE 1.19D. Calculate 746 divided by 142, 38.5, 17.3, and 1255.

Solution: Set the right index of CI to 746 on D

> Move the hairline to the several denominator values on CI
> Read the respective answers on D as 5.25, 19.9, 43.1, and 0.594

EXAMPLE 1.19E. Calculate: $\dfrac{100}{14 \times 710}, \dfrac{100}{14 \times 644}, \dfrac{100}{14 \times 581}, \dfrac{100}{14 \times 470}$.

This example is the same type as Example 1.19D, although at first glance it may not appear to be. The ratio, 100/14, is a common term divided by several different denominator quantities, and the CI and D scales may be used to obtain the results with one slide setting. The ratio, 100/14, may be obtained by using C and D scales.

Solution: Set 14 on C to the left index of D (100)

> Move the hairline on CI to: 710, 644, 581, and 470
> Read on D: 0.01007, 0.0111, 0.0123, and 0.0152
> See Fig. 1.28

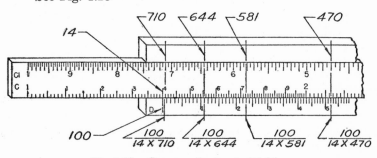

Fig. 1.28. Common Factors in Division

Example 1.19E: $\dfrac{100}{14 \times 710} = 0.01007$; $\dfrac{100}{14 \times 644} = 0.0111$; $\dfrac{100}{14 \times 581} = 0.0123$;

$$\dfrac{100}{14 \times 470} = 0.0152$$

EXAMPLE 1.19F.   Calculate the following:

$$\frac{1}{0.0645 \times 76 \times 2.54}, \quad \frac{1}{0.0645 \times 82.5 \times 2.54}, \quad \frac{1}{0.0645 \times 95.5 \times 2.54}.$$

A common term in these three expressions is $1/(0.0645 \times 2.54)$.   This can be reduced to 6.1.   Then $6.1/76$, $6.1/82.5$, and $6.1/95.5$ may all be computed with one setting of the slide using CI and D scales as in Example 1.19E.

The examples in this article suggest: (1) search out common factors and select a method of solution which requires minimum number of settings of the slide; (2) look for repeated digits, to save reading the same setting twice; (3) complete all calculations using one index before reversing the slide; (4) make related computations in tabular form.

All of these examples may be reduced to a constant term with a succession of numbers multiplied by it, or divided into it.   If it is a series of divisions, the CI and D scales lead to minimum setting; if it is a series of multiplications, the C and D scales lead to minimum settings.   If folded scales are available, reversal of the slide may be avoided.   See Art. 1.20.

The time-saving value of these suggestions may not be noticeable when the number of calculations is small, as in these examples.   However, in longer problems, such as some in Part II, the saving in time is appreciable. It is a good plan to practice the fastest method even on short problems.

1.20. Folded Logarithmic Scales.   A folded logarithmic scale is one for which the beginning or end graduation is not a power of 10.   This topic of folded scales is placed near the end of the chapter because not all slide rules carry folded scales, and it is desired to make as much of the material as possible applicable to the greatest number of different slide rules.   Of the commonly used slide rules shown in the Appendix, Figs., A.1 to A.8, pages 182–189, folded scales are found on all but one, the Mannheim type, Fig. A.1.

Logarithmic scales may be "folded" at any number.   One of the commonly used points of fold is π, the ratio of circle circumference to diameter. This is the point of fold on the CF and DF scales of Figs. A.2 and A.3.

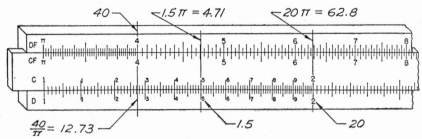

Fig. 1.29.   Folded Scales for Multiplication or Division by π
Examples: $1.5\pi = 4.71$; $20\pi = 62.8$; $40/\pi = 12.73$

Thus, by setting the hairline to any number on D, π times D may be read on the DF scale. Similarly, for any number on C, π times C may be read on CF, as shown in Fig. 1.29. Conversely, $1/\pi$ times numbers set on DF are found on D.

The CIF scale is folded at $1/\pi$ and, as the name implies, it is a C scale inverted and folded, so that $1/\pi$ times a number on CI may be read on the CIF scale.

The Deci-LogLog slide rule, Fig. A.5, has in addition to CF and DF scales a set of folded scales marked CF/$_M$ and DF/$_M$. The point of

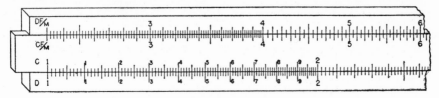

Fig. 1.30.   Folded Scales: CF/$_M$ and DF/$_M$
Point of fold, 2.303

fold is 2.303, Fig. 1.30. This set of folded scales may be used for some of the same purposes as other folded scales. The reason for selecting 2.303 as a fold point is explained in Chapter 4 on logarithmic and exponential calculations.

The CF and DF scales, folded at π, are useful in particular applications involving circles, some trigonometry problems, and special formulas of engineering. But probably the most common general use of any folded scales is to complete a continued division or multiplication without the need for reversing indices.

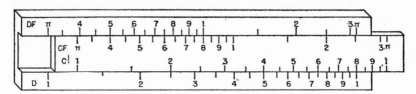

Fig. 1.31.   Folded Scale Relationship: Partially Graduated Scales
Example: 4 on C at 5 on D; 6 on C at 7.5 on D;
4 on CF at 5 on DF; 6 on CF at 7.5 on DF; etc.

It will be observed in Fig. 1.31 that for any setting of C relative to D, the CF scale has the same relationship to DF. That is, if 4 on C is matched with 5 on D, then 4 on CF matches 5 on DF. Thus, if a particular reading on D against some number on C is off the scale, the reading may be obtained by setting the hairline to the number on CF and reading on the DF scale.

EXAMPLE 1.20A. Calculate $7 \times 9.5/6$.

Solution: Calculate 7/6 by setting 6 on C to 7 on D
        At 9.5 on CF read 11.1 on DF
        See Fig. 1.32

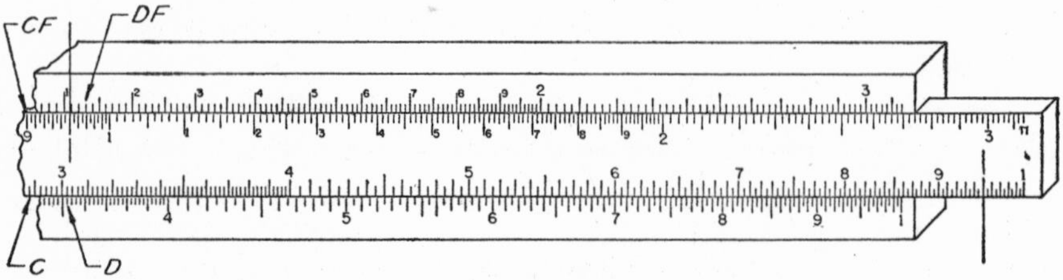

Fig. 1.32. Folded Scales for Continued Division and Multiplication)
Example 1.20A: $7 \times 9.5/6 = 11.1$

EXAMPLE 1.20B. Calculate $7 \times 9/4$

Solution: Perform 7/4 by setting 4 on C to 7 on D
        At 9 on CF read 15.75 on DF

If 9/4 is attempted first using C and D scales, multiplication by 7 is off
scale, and the use of folded scales or reversal of indices on C is necessary.
    EXAMPLE 1.20C. A problem suggested in Art. 1.16 but not solved
there is:

$$\frac{95 \times 42 \times 81 \times 12}{75 \times 31 \times 19}$$

Using folded scales, this may be carried out without reversal of indices
and in the sequence the numbers appear.

Solution: The scales on which the numbers are set are indicated by subscripts, and the position of the intermediate partial answers is noted at
breaks in the fraction bar.

$$\frac{95_D}{75_C} \; D \; \frac{42_C}{31_C} \; D \; \frac{81_{CF}}{19_{CF}} \; DF \; \frac{12_{CF}}{} = 87.8_{DF}$$

In long problems like this, pursuing the intermediate answers from
one scale to another must be carefully watched.[4]
    EXAMPLE 1.20D. Calculate 73/37, 63/37, 53/37, 43/37, 33/37, 23/37.

Solution: Calculate 1/37 by setting 37 on C to the right index of D; move
the hairline to the several numerator values on CF or C and read the

---

[4] A procedure for using folded and normal scales for division and multiplication
called the "center-drift method" is recommended by Lee H. Johnson in *The Slide
Rule*, page 42. (New York: Van Nostrand, 1949.) Essentially it consists in choosing
folded, normal, or inverted scales for the successive steps in such a way that the
settings and intermediate partial answers are near the middle portion of the frame.

corresponding DF or D scale as follows: 1.97, 1.70, 1.43, 1.16, 0.892, and 0.622. If 37 on C is set to the left index of D, less than one-half of the slide will be within the scale limits, and in particular 33/37 will not be obtainable without reversal of indices whether CF and DF or C and D scales are tried.

EXAMPLE 1.20E. Calculate 26/9.1, 26/7.2, 26/3.3, 26/2.4, 26/1.5 using one slide setting only.

Solution: Set the left index of CI to 26 on D; at 9.1, 7.2, and 3.3 on CI read 2.86, 3.61, and 7.88 respectively on D; at 2.4 and 1.5 on CIF read 10.8 and 17.3 on DF. If attempted with a slide rule not equipped with CIF scale, reversal of indices is necessary for the latter two calculations.

EXAMPLE 1.20F. Calculate 6.2 × 0.068/370.

Solution: Set 370 on C to 0.068 on D
At 6.2 on CF read 114 on DF

For the decimal point position

$$\frac{6.2 \times 0.068}{370} = \frac{\overset{0}{6.2} \times \overset{-2}{6.8}}{\underset{+2}{3.70}} = \overset{-4}{11.4} = 0.00114$$

EXAMPLE 1.20G. Calculate 2.2/(3.4 × 0.7).

Solution: Perform 2.2/3.4 by setting 3.4 on C to 2.2 on **D**
At 0.7 on CIF read 0.925 on DF.

Division by the 0.7 might be performed by moving the hairline to 0.7 on CI and reading on D. However, it is off scale, so CIF and DF are used.

EXAMPLE 1.20H. Calculate 3.7 × 1.65 × 1.49.

Solution: Set the hairline to 3.7 on D
Move the slide to place 1.65 on CI beneath the hairline
At 1.49 on CF read 9.10 on DF

As an alternate method

Set the hairline to 3.7 on D
Move the slide to place 1.65 on CIF beneath the hairline
At 1.49 on CF read 9.10 on D.

EXAMPLE 1.20I. Calculate $\dfrac{1}{3.2 \times 7.1 \times 0.0048}$. This example cannot be solved in one slide setting using any of the commercial slide rules discussed here. The best method of solution probably is to calculate 3.2 × 71. × 0.0048 using D, CI, CF, and DF, then take the reciprocal in a separate operation. The answer is **9.17.**

The foregoing examples illustrate typical problems for which folded scales make it possible to obtain a solution with one slide setting. Without folded scales these problems require at least one reversal of indices.

1.21. Summary, Chapter 1. This summary is intended to remind the reader of the fact that the many examples, illustrations, and problems in this chapter demonstrate variations of one simple principle.

Brief statements on methods of operation, accuracy, and decimal point location are intended to refresh the memory of those who may discontinue the use of the slide rule for a time and then resume it. Parenthetical references also are included to the articles or illustrations describing the topic in greater detail.

1. *Principle.* The slide rule performs division or multiplication by mechanically subtracting or adding lengths proportional to the logarithms of numbers (Art. 1.2, Fig. 1.3).

In algebraic form, if

$$N = 10^p$$
$$M = 10^q$$

then

$$p = \log N$$
$$q = \log M$$

and

$$p + q = \log N + \log M = \log (N \times M)$$
$$p - q = \log N - \log M = \log \frac{N}{M}$$

The lengths subtracted or added on the slide rule correspond to p and q, but the scales are graduated with the numbers, M and N (Figs. 1.12, 1.17).

A problem in continued division and multiplication is a succession of such logarithmic subtractions and additions, the answer to one step being the first factor in the next operation, generally without reading the intermediate answer (Art. 1.16, Fig. 1.19).

2. *Recognition of Logarithmic Scales* (Art. 1.4). The logarithmic scales suitable for performing division or multiplication may be identified on any slide rule by observing if the distance from 1 to 2 is about 30 per cent of the cycle length from 1 to 10 (Art. 1.3). Two logarithmic scales with the same cycle length, one on the slide and one on the frame, are used for performing division or multiplication.

3. *Scale Graduations* (Fig. 1.5). On 10-inch logarithmic scales, the finest graduation subdivision intervals usually are: 0.01, 0.02, or 0.05. Hence, the graduations next lower and higher than 2 are 1.99 and 2.02; the graduations next lower and higher than 4 are 3.98 and 4.05 (Art. 1.6).

4. *Accuracy* (Art. 1.15). A slide rule reading which is correct to one-fifth of the finest subdivision interval thus may represent an error of between one-tenth and one-fourth of one per cent. With care, an accuracy of reading and setting of this magnitude is attainable, although the accuracy to be expected decreases with the number of factors in the problem.

One additional significant figure can be obtained readily in simple division or multiplication by splitting one of the factors into two parts and performing one part of the calculation mentally and the other part with the slide rule (Art. 1.15).

For example, the product

$$F \times G = (F_1 + F_2)G = (F_1G)_m + (F_2G)_s$$

where the subscript, m, indicates the operation performed mentally and subscript, s, indicates the operation performed with slide rule.

In a similar way

$$\frac{N}{M} = \frac{N_1 + N_2}{M} + \frac{N_1}{M_m} + \frac{N_2}{M_s}$$

The quantity, N or F, should be split so that N_1 or F_1 is large compared to N_2 or F_2, and thus the mental arithmetic is easily performed (Art. 1.15).

5. *Manipulation of the Slide Rule.* In holding the slide rule, one should avoid squeezing the frame so the slide binds. Better control and more accurate setting are obtained if one hand opposes the motion of the slide being made by the other hand (Art. 1.8, Figs. 1.9, 1.10, 1.11).

6. *Operation Procedure.* The method of operation for performing division, or logarithmic subtraction, is: C and D scales (Arts. 1.9, 1.11, Figs. 1.12, 1.14).

Set the hairline to the numerator on D
Place the denominator on C beneath the hairline
Read the quotient on D opposite the index

CI and D scales (Art. 1.18; Fig. 1.28)

Set the index of CI to the numerator on D
Place the hairline to the denominator on CI
Read the quotient on D beneath the hairline

Conversely, multiplication, being a logarithmic addition, may be performed by interchanging the above methods of operation. C and D scales (Art. 1.13; Fig. 1.17)

Set the index of C to the first factor on D
Move the hairline to the second factor on C
Read the product on D beneath the hairline

CI and D scales (Art. 1.18; Fig. 1.25)

> Set the hairline to the first factor on D
> Place the second factor on CI beneath the hairline
> Read the product on D opposite the index

7. *Folded Scales* (Art. 1.20; Figs. 1.29–1.32).   In any one of the above operating statements, folded scales may be used throughout.   That is, DF, CF, and CIF may be used for D, C, and CI.   It should be noted, however, that the index of the folded scales is near the middle rather than at the end.

Also, the quantity set on the slide may be on a folded scale if the answer is read on the corresponding folded scale on the frame.   That is, for example

> Set the index of C to the first factor on D
> Move the hairline to the second factor on CF
> Read the product on DF beneath the hairline

and

> Set the index of CI to the numerator on D
> Place the hairline to the denominator on CIF
> Read the quotient on DF beneath the hairline

8. *Common Factors* (Art. 1.19, Fig. 1.28).   Problems in which one numerator or denominator quantity takes on a series of values while other terms remain fixed may be solved with one slide setting, or sometimes two slide settings if folded scales are not used.   That is, if k represents the constant term, and x_1, x_2, x_3, . . . represent the successive values of the variable, four typical situations are:

(a) kx_1, kx_2, kx_3, . . .

(b) $\dfrac{x_1}{k'}, \dfrac{x_2}{k'}, \dfrac{x_3}{k'}, \cdots$, or if $k = 1/k'$ this is like (a)

(c) $\dfrac{k}{x_1}, \dfrac{k}{x_2}, \dfrac{k}{x_3}, \cdots$

(d) $\dfrac{1}{k'x_1}, \dfrac{1}{k'x_2}, \dfrac{1}{k'x_3}, \cdots$, or $\dfrac{k}{x_1}, \dfrac{k}{x_2}, \dfrac{k}{x_3}, \cdots$ if $k = 1/k'$

For (a) then

> Set the index of C to the constant term, k
> Move the hairline to successive values of x on C (or CF)
> Read the products on D (or DF)

For (b)

> Find $1/k'$ and carry out as for (a)

And for (c)

> Set the index of CI to k on D
> Move the hairline to successive values of x on CI (or CIF)
> Read the quotients on D (or DF)

For (d)

> Find $1/k'$ and carry out like (c)

The quantity, k or k', may be given as a product or quotient of several numbers; these may be reduced to a single number first.

9. *Decimal Point.* Two methods are suggested for placing the decimal point (Art. 1.10).

SIMILAR SIMPLE NUMBER SCHEME

a. Round off the given numbers to numbers having one digit and zeros.
b. By cancellation and mental approximation, determine the approximate answer.
c. Place the decimal point in the digits read from the slide rule to correspond with this mental approximation.

STANDARD NUMBER METHOD

a. Write each number as a standard number, that is, with the decimal point following the first digit.
b. Note the correction number for each, that is, the number of places which the decimal point must be moved to form the standard number, calling a move to the left, $+$, and a move to the right, $-$.
c. Determine the resultant correction number by algebraically adding all numerator correction numbers and subtracting all denominator correction numbers.
d. Using the rounded off one digit numbers, determine decimal point position by mental approximation.
e. Apply the correction number in reverse to the result obtained for the standard numbers.

1.22. Problems on Chapter 1.

1S	1T	1U	1V

Calculate the following to 4 significant figures using slide rule and mental arithmetic.

	1S	1T	1U	1V
a	$\dfrac{1785}{1625}$	$\dfrac{6237}{7.468}$	$\dfrac{8595}{7481}$	$\dfrac{0.1277}{8.752}$
b	$\dfrac{2.062}{19.82}$	$\dfrac{52.27}{248.5}$	$\dfrac{0.9247}{3042}$	$\dfrac{127.65}{5278}$
c	15.15×40.73	216.7×0.04875	0.7352×52.65	1176×0.6375
d	2622×8.032	1232×0.8623	3682×5.081	6145×4187

1S   1T   1U   1V

Calculate the following using minimum slide movement. Note that it is possible to solve any of these problems in one slide setting using certain of the commercial slide rules shown in the Appendix. The problems provide good practice even if several slide settings are required.

e $\dfrac{1}{527}$	$\dfrac{1}{0.93}$	$\dfrac{1}{0.082}$	$\dfrac{1}{8790}$
f $\dfrac{1}{7.26}$	$\dfrac{1}{43.2}$	$\dfrac{1}{0.0052}$	$\dfrac{1}{6.05}$
g $\pi \times 1.06$	$\pi \times 79.5$	$\pi \times 0.085$	$\pi \times 16.8$
h $\dfrac{152}{\pi}$	$\dfrac{3.76}{\pi}$	$\dfrac{0.935}{\pi}$	$\dfrac{0.027}{\pi}$
i $\dfrac{37 \times 84}{526}$	$\dfrac{2.09 \times 3.42}{7.46}$	$\dfrac{0.92 \times 855}{0.615}$	$\dfrac{575 \times 72}{41.4}$
j $\dfrac{36.2 \times 19}{0.895}$	$\dfrac{162 \times 138}{0.43}$	$\dfrac{275 \times 304}{86}$	$\dfrac{0.106 \times 92}{99}$
k $3.3 \times 7.1 \times 13$	$0.26 \times 48 \times 61$	$42 \times 47 \times 5.5$	$6.7 \times 1.77 \times 9$
l $0.17 \times 410 \times 139$	$9.6 \times 1.8 \times 75$	$36 \times 93 \times 4$	$72 \times 4.1 \times 4.4$
m $\dfrac{1}{2.4 \times 8.2 \times 3}$	$\dfrac{1}{5.2 \times 3.1 \times 6}$	$\dfrac{1}{8 \times 3.7 \times 1.79}$	$\dfrac{1}{1.42 \times 6.9 \times 51}$
n $\dfrac{1}{76 \times 17 \times 41}$	$\dfrac{1}{0.7 \times 0.34 \times 15}$	$\dfrac{1}{26 \times 27 \times 28}$	$\dfrac{1}{10.7 \times 182 \times 77}$

Calculate the following using minimum slide movement. Note that it is possible to solve any of these problems in two slide settings.

o $\dfrac{372 \times 97}{126 \times 21.2}$	$\dfrac{42 \times 4.1 \times 17}{65}$	$\dfrac{23}{68 \times 42 \times 51}$	$\dfrac{162 \times 56}{97 \times 82}$
p $\dfrac{8.62 \times 46}{1.70 \times 16.9}$	$\dfrac{106 \times 62 \times 36}{85}$	$\dfrac{208}{34 \times 14 \times 36}$	$\dfrac{242 \times 21}{76 \times 92}$
q $17 \times 9.1 \times 31 \times 19$	$\dfrac{8.72 \times 19.5}{605 \times 1.37}$	$\dfrac{23 \times 30.3}{7.65 \times 83}$	$70 \times 104 \times 3.8 \times 11$
r $\dfrac{322 \times 1.89}{20.5 \times 3.7}$	$\dfrac{29.6}{0.3 \times 1.72 \times 1.55}$	$\dfrac{4.05 \times 3.92}{128 \times 0.505}$	$\dfrac{725 \times 155}{1.27 \times 4.03}$

Determine decimal point position only in the answer.

s $\dfrac{1}{0.0036 \times 432} = 643$	$7650 \times 8300 = 635$	$\dfrac{0.00123}{895} = 1375$	$\dfrac{260}{375 \times 0.011} = 63$
t $\dfrac{746 \times 0.29}{0.0086} = 252$	$\dfrac{0.385}{190 \times 250} = 81$	$\dfrac{1}{27 \times 460} = 805$	$\dfrac{4.35}{700 \times 870} = 714$

1W

Solve for U, V, W, in the following proportions:

$$\text{a} \quad \frac{3.7}{U} = \frac{52}{V} = \frac{0.95}{W} = \frac{150}{21}$$

$$\text{b} \quad \frac{455}{0.95} = \frac{7.60}{U} = \frac{V}{920} = \frac{0.03}{W}$$

1W

$$\text{c} \quad \frac{0.85}{U} = \frac{V}{75.0} = \frac{75}{0.14} = \frac{W}{305}$$

$$\text{d} \quad \frac{0.37}{U} = \frac{520}{0.92} = \frac{V}{175} = \frac{W}{4.20}$$

Using minimum slide setting for each group calculate the following:

e $\dfrac{\pi x}{180}$ $(x = 305;\ 17.2;\ 840;\ 7040)$

f $\dfrac{295x}{132}$ $(x = 38.5;\ 780;\ 6.05;\ 1280)$

g $0.905x$ $(x = 107;\ 427;\ 840;\ 221)$
h $0.042x$ $(x = 45;\ 226;\ 187;\ 820)$

i $\dfrac{8.75}{x}$ $(x = 272;\ 0.088;\ 32.4;\ 927)$

j $\dfrac{0.13}{x}$ $(x = 12.2;\ 1.78;\ 475;\ 0.115)$

k $\dfrac{1}{12x}$ $(x = 8.75;\ 23.5;\ 128;\ 0.92)$

l $\dfrac{1}{3.9x}$ $(x = 232;\ 16.2;\ 6.75;\ 805)$

Calculate and prepare graphs on uniform coordinate paper for each of the following, showing calculations in tabular form.

m Resistance, R, versus electric current, I, for a voltage, E, of 110 volts. Use R scale in ohms, 2 to 20; I in amperes, 5 to 55; $R = E/I$.
n Speed versus time for a distance of 500 miles. S in mph, 100 to 125; T in hours and minutes, 4 to 5 hrs; $S = D/T$.
o Electrical conductance, G, versus resistance R. R in ohms, 0 to 100; G in mhos, 0 to 0.2. $G = 1/R$.

Chapter

2

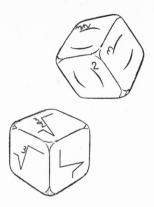

SIMPLE POWERS AND ROOTS

2.1. Theory of Scale Construction. As mentioned in Chapter 1, it is possible to learn operating procedures for slide rule calculations without a knowledge of the theory of scale construction. However, more rapid learning and greater facility in acquiring new skills are possible if the theory is understood. Consequently, as a general plan of organization in each chapter, both the general theory of and operating procedures for particular commercial slide rules are presented. This article is devoted principally to the theory.

Mechanically, the principle of operation for most of the problems of this chapter is simply to "equate lengths," or, to set on one slide rule scale and read on another. In other words, no movement of the slide is required for simple powers and roots.

In algebraic terms, if

$$U = N \times N = N^2$$

then

$$\log U = \log N + \log N = \log N^2 = 2 \log N \tag{2.1}$$

or

$$\frac{1}{2} \log U = \log N \tag{2.2}$$

Thus, to read squares of numbers directly from a slide rule a pair of related logarithmic scales for N and U is required on which the scale factors (in simple terms, the distances from 1 to 10) are in the ratio of $1/2:1$, or $1:2$, corresponding to the coefficients of log U and log N in Eq. (2.1) or (2.2).

This condition is fulfilled on each of the selected commercial slide rules, Figs. A.1 to A.8, pages 182–189.   The A and B scales shown on some of the slide rules have a cycle length one-half that of the basic C or D scales, Fig. 2.1.   Thus, if one thinks in terms of the full-length C or D scale as the unit scale with coefficient 1, then $\frac{1}{2}$ log U corresponds to the A or B scale, and log N corresponds to the C or D scale.

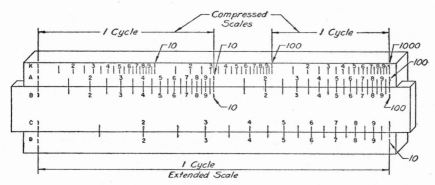

Fig. 2.1.   Scale Designations and Their Cycle Lengths on Simple Power and Root Scales

Scales: K, A, B, C, and D

The $\sqrt{}$ scale of Fig. A.5 and the R scale of Fig. A.7 are twice as long as the basic D scale, and are folded at $\sqrt{10}$, Fig. 2.2.   Eq. (2.1) is the form of equation appropriate for these slide rules.

In a similar manner, if

$$K = M \times M \times M = M^3$$

then

$$\log K = \log M + \log M + \log M = \log M^3 = 3 \log M \qquad (2.3)$$

or

$$\frac{1}{3} \log K = \log M \qquad (2.4)$$

Eq. (2.4) is the basis for the K and D scales found on several of the commercial slide rules shown in the Appendix, pages 182–189, and illustrated with partially graduated scales in Fig. 2.1.   Eq. (2.3) is the basis for the $\sqrt[3]{}$ scales of Figs. A.5 and 2.2.

It is interesting to note that if the A scale from one slide rule and the $\sqrt{}$ scale from the other should be placed on the same slide rule, fourth powers and roots could be found with a direct setting.   The K and $\sqrt[3]{}$

scales would enable one to read ninth powers and roots. The Versalog slide rule, Fig. A.7, includes a K scale, and R scales like the $\sqrt{}$ scales. This combination permits the direct solution of sixth powers and roots.

2.2. Graduation of Scales. The various log scales discussed in Chapter 1 when applied to a 10-inch slide rule are all graduated the same and in the manner shown in Fig. 1.5.

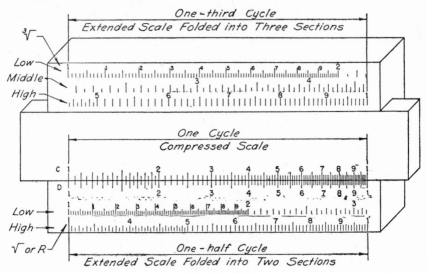

Fig. 2.2. Scale Designations and Their Cycle Lengths on Simple Power and Root Scales

Scales: $\sqrt[3]{}$, C and D, $\sqrt{}$ or R

As shown in Figs. 2.1 and 2.2, the additional scales for squares, cubes, square roots, and cube roots described in Art. 2.1 vary in their length for one cycle (1 to 10) from one-third to three times the C and D scale length. Obviously, for readability and accuracy the manner of subdivision on all these scales cannot be the same as on C and D.

Figs. 2.3 and 2.4 illustrate in diagrammatic form the general plan for graduation of these scales. As on C and D, there are three different graduation intervals in a cycle, but the point of changeover is different.

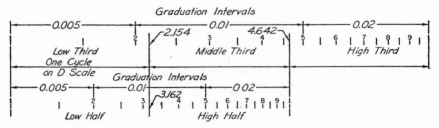

Fig. 2.3. Graduation Plan for Folded Simple Power and Root Scales

On 10-inch C and D scales the changeover is made at 2 and 4, whereas the several scales indicated in Figs. 2.3 and 2.4 show changeover at 2 or 3 and 5 or 6.

Several examples of setting numbers on these scales are proposed, described, and illustrated in Figs. 2.5 to 2.8. These examples intentionally avoid decimal point difficulties and adhere to one cycle only of A and K scales, thus focusing attention on the scale reading.

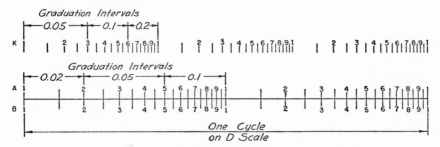

Fig. 2.4. Graduation Plan for Non-Folded Simple Power and Root Scales

It is suggested that the reader attempt to make the setting on his slide rule without reference to the illustration and description. After making the setting, a comparison with the description and illustration should reveal any errors; this procedure should lead to more rapid correction of faults in scale reading.

EXAMPLE 2.2A. Set 1.82 on A. *Solution:* The setting is about one-eighth of the way along the A scale; the finest graduation interval

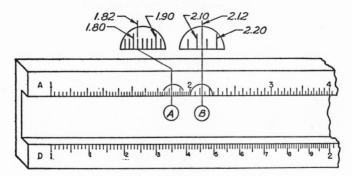

Fig. 2.5.   Scale Settings on the A Scale
Examples: 2.2A:1.82; 2.2B:2.12

represents 0.02 in this portion; 1.8 is two minor graduations to the left of 2; and 1.82 is one finest graduation to the right on 1.8.   See Fig. 2.5.

EXAMPLE 2.2B. Set 2.12 on A. *Solution:* The setting is approximately one-sixth of the way along the scale; the finest graduation interval represents 0.05 in this portion; therefore, 2.1 is two graduations from 2;

and 2.15 is three graduations from 2; and 2.12 is estimated at two-fifths of the way from 2.1 to 2.15.   See Fig. 2.5.

EXAMPLE 2.2C.   Set 1.82 on K.   *Solution:* The graduation interval in this portion of K is 0.05; and 1.82 is two-fifths of the distance between 1.8 and 1.85.   See Fig. 2.6.

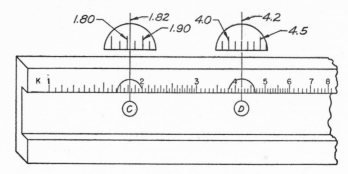

Fig. 2.6.   Scale Settings on the K Scale
Examples: 2.2C: 1.82; 2.2D: 4.2

EXAMPLE 2.2D.   Set 4.2 on K.   *Solution:* This setting is approximately one-fifth of the way along the K scale.   See Fig. 2.6.

EXAMPLE 2.2E.   Set 2.42 on $\sqrt{}$ or R_1.   *Solution:* This setting is approximately three-fourths of the way along the slide rule.   Since this complete scale is twice as long as D, more graduations can be inserted than on D; in this portion of the scale there are twice as many graduations

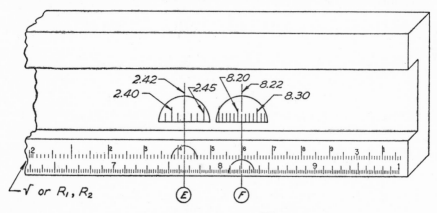

Fig. 2.7.   Scale Settings on $\sqrt{}$ or R Scale
Examples: 2.2E: 2.42; 2.2F: 8.22

as on D.   The finest graduation interval represents 0.01, the small 4 represents 2.4, and two graduations from 2.4 represents 2.42.   See Fig. 2.7.

EXAMPLE 2.2F. Set 8.22 on $\sqrt{}$ or R₂. *Solution:* This setting is approximately four-fifths of the way along the slide rule; the finest graduation interval represents 0.02 in this portion; 8.2 is two minor graduations from 8, and 8.22 is one graduation from 8.2. See Fig. 2.7.

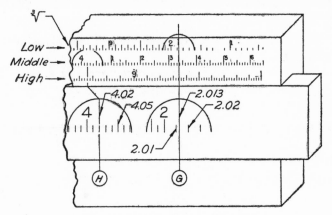

Fig. 2.8. Scale Settings on $\sqrt[3]{}$ Scale
Examples: 2.2G: 2.013; 2.2H: 4.02

EXAMPLE 2.2G. Set 2.013 on $\sqrt[3]{}$. *Solution:* The $\sqrt[3]{}$ scale is graduated the same as the $\sqrt{}$ scale; the description of the setting is similar to Example 2.2B. The first graduation to the right of 2 is 2.01 on $\sqrt[3]{}$. See Fig. 2.8.

EXAMPLE 2.2H. Set 4.02 on $\sqrt[3]{}$. *Solution:* This setting is in the middle section of the scale near the right end; the minor graduation and the small 1 to the right of 4 represents 4.1; two finest graduations from 4 represents 4.02. See Fig. 2.8.

The graduation characteristics for the simple power scales on various 10-inch commercial slide rules frequently are like one of the following:

Scale Name	Cycle Length	Range	Grad. Interval	Range	Grad. Interval	Range	Grad. Interval
K	1/3	1–3	0.05	3–6	0.1	6–10	0.2
K	1/3	1–2	0.02	2–5	0.05	5–10	0.2
A	1/2	1–2	0.02	2–5	0.05	5–10	0.2
D	1	1–2	0.01	2–5	0.02	5–10	0.05
$\sqrt{}$ or R	2	1–2	0.005	2–5	0.01	5–10	0.02
$\sqrt[3]{}$	3	1–2	0.005	2–5	0.01	5–10	0.02

2.3. Squares. Variations among different makes of slide rules are slight with regard to the manner of placing and marking the full-length logarithmic scales. Important differences are sometimes found in the arrangement and notation of the scales for simple powers and roots, Figs.

2.3 and 2.4.   However, the basic requirement for squares and square roots is a pair of related logarithmic scales on which the length of a cycle on one scale of the pair is twice as great as on the other.

A single statement of the method of operation which is applicable to all forms of slide rules is:

> Set the number, N, on the expanded scale of the related pair of log scales
>
> Read the square, U, on the compressed scale (a scale factor one-half as great as the expanded scale)

It would be possible to devise a scale arrangement as indicated in Fig. 2.9 which would give the decimal point position directly.   However, the accuracy would be poor or the length must be great; hence, the more satisfactory plan is to determine decimal point position independently

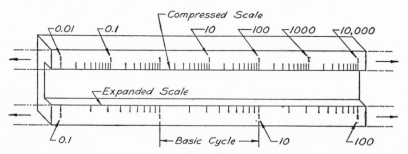

Fig. 2.9.   Model of Slide Rule for Direct Reading of Decimal Point Position in Square Roots or Squares

of the slide rule, just as in Chapter 1.   Again, either the "similar simple number scheme" or the "standard number" method may be used. Several descriptive examples show both methods.

EXAMPLE 2.3A.   Calculate 324^2.

Solution:

Set to 3.24 on D   Set glass to 3.24 on $\sqrt{}$ or R_2
Read 10.5 on A   Read 10.5 on D

For placing the decimal point

$$324^2 = \overset{+2}{(3.24)^2} = \overset{+2}{3.24} \times \overset{+2}{3.24} = \overset{+4}{10.5} = 105{,}000$$

or note that

$$300^2 = 90{,}000$$

EXAMPLE 2.3B. Calculate 0.0187^2.

Solution:

Set glass to 1.87 on D   Set glass to 1.87 on $\sqrt{}$ or R_1
Read 3.50 on A   Read 3.50 on D

For placing the decimal point

$$0.0187^2 = (1.87)^2 \overset{-2}{=} 3.5 \overset{-4}{=} 0.00035$$

or note that

$$0.02^2 = 0.0004$$

The 2:1 ratio test, described in Art. 1.4, may be used to recognize logarithmic scales on any slide rule. Comparison of the length of a cycle (1 to 10), which in the case of squares is also 2:1, is equally easy. Therefore, if one has a slide rule with the scales marked differently, by identifying those log scales having a length ratio of 2:1, the operations described here can be carried out.

The general algebraic equation to be solved in finding either squares or square roots is

$$U_A = N_D{}^2; \frac{1}{2} \log U_A = \log N_D \qquad (2.2)$$

The subscripts denote the slide rule scales on the frame constructed for these quantities. Therefore, to find the square of a number between 1

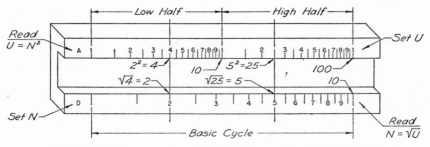

Fig. 2.10. Squares of One-Digit Numbers on Non-Folded Scales

and 10 using one of these slide rules, as shown in Fig. 2.10

Set the number, N, on D
Read the square, U, on the A scale

Since the B scale matches A, and the C scale matches D, B and C may be substituted for A and D. Or, if the index of C is aligned with the index of D, then A may be used with C or D, and B with C or D. Aligning indices in this way may avoid the need for turning a slide rule over to read the square. Some slide rules are made which do not include A and D scales on the same side, or B and C scales on the same side.

The slide rules shown in Figs. A.5 and A.7 are based upon the slightly different form of Eq. (2.2)

$$U_D = N\sqrt{}^{-2} \text{ or } U_D = N_R{}^2$$

and

$$\log U_D = 2 \log N\sqrt{} \text{ or } \log U_D = 2 \log N_R \qquad (2.1)$$

Thus, to find the square of a number between 1 and 10 using one of these slide rules, as shown in Fig. 2.11

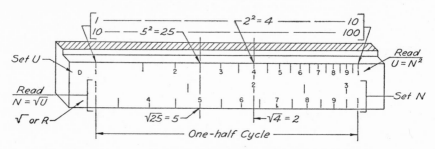

Fig. 2.11. Squares of One-Digit Numbers on Folded Scales

Set N on $\sqrt{}$ or R; read $U = N^2$ on D
Examples: $2^2 = 4$; $5^2 = 25$

Set the number, N, on the $\sqrt{}$ or R scale
Read the square, U, on D

EXAMPLE 2.3C. Calculate 5.2^{-2}. *Solution:* Since $5.2^{-2} = 1/(5.2)^2$ one may calculate 5.2^2 then find the reciprocal. A shorter method is:

Set the hairline to 5.2 on CI   Set to 5.2 on $\sqrt{}$ or R_2
$1/5.2$ appears on C 5.2^2 appears on D
Read $1/(5.2)^2$ on B as 0.037   Read $1/(5.2)^2$ on DI as 0.037

or

Set the hairline to 5.2 on $\sqrt{}$ or R_2
5.2^2 appears on D
Match index of CI with index of D
Read $1/(5.2)^2$ on CI as 0.037

Since to square a number means to multiply it by itself, it is apparent that another method for solving any of these problems is to use C and D scales, or CI and D scales, as described for multiplication in Chapter 1.

2.4. Square Roots. The algebraic equation

$$U = N^2; \log U = 2 \log N \qquad (2.1)$$

may be solved for U if N is known; such is the topic of Art. 2.3.   Or, it may be solved for N if U is known.   It is a laborious task to find square root by the usual arithmetical methods.   A slide rule makes it as easy as squaring a number.   From the theory of Art. 2.1, it may be observed that the method of operation is:

> Set the number, U, on the compressed scale of the related pair of log scales
> Read its square root, N, on the expanded scale (scale factor twice that of the compressed scale)

In specific terms applicable to the A and D scales:

> Set the hairline to the number, U, on A
> Read N, its square root, on D

Although both cycles of the A scale are often numbered alike with one-digit numbers only, it should be observed that when taking square roots of numbers between 1 and 100, the right cycle (high half) must represent numbers from 10 to 100, as shown in Fig. 2.10.   The left cycle (low half) represents numbers from 1 to 10.

EXAMPLE 2.4A.   Calculate $\sqrt{2.12}$.

Solution:

Set to 2.12 on low half of A   Set the hairline to 2.12 on D
Read 1.455 on D   Read 1.455 on R_1 or $\sqrt{}$ (low half)

EXAMPLE 2.4B.   Calculate $\sqrt{75}$, or $(75)^{\frac{1}{2}}$.

Solution:

Set to 75 on high half of A   Set the hairline to 75 on D
Read 8.66 on D   Read 8.66 on R_2 or $\sqrt{}$ (high half)

Obviously, $\sqrt{7.5}$ could be read on the other half of the scale as 2.74.

For numbers 100 times as large as these examples, the square roots would be $\sqrt{100}$, or 10, times as large.   For numbers 0.0001 times as large, the square roots would be 0.01 times as large.   Fig. 2.12 shows, for a range of numbers, this change in decimal point position and the corresponding decimal point position of the square root.   This table could be extended indefinitely to larger and smaller values.   The information of Fig. 2.12 may be summarized by the general statement:

> *In taking square roots the middle index of the A scale represents odd powers of 10.*

The same relationship illustrated in Fig. 2.10 must exist for $\sqrt{}$ or R scale.   That is, numbers shown set on the low half of A will be set on

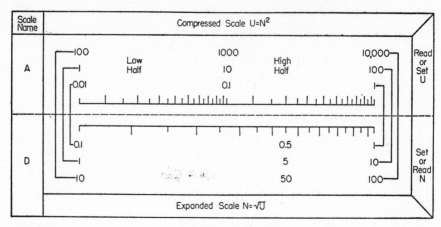

Fig. 2.12. Diagram of Operation and Decimal Point Location for Squares and Square Roots on Non-Folded Scales

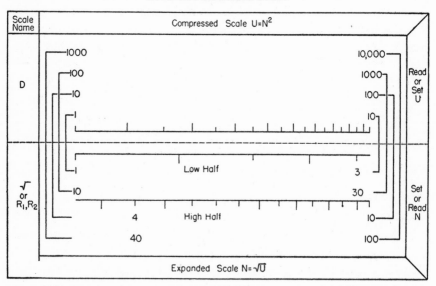

Fig. 2.13. Diagram of Operation and Decimal Point Location for Squares and Square Roots on Folded Scales

D and their square roots found on R_1 or $\sqrt{}$ (low half). See Figs. 2.12 and 2.13.

The tabular information of Fig. 2.13 may be generalized as follows:

The point of fold of the $\sqrt{}$ or R scale represents the square root of odd powers of 10.

The correction number method provides an equivalent, and sometimes easier, way for determining which half of the scale to use, and it also aids in placing the decimal point.

1. Move the decimal point an even number of places to form a number between 1 and 100.

2. Write the associated correction number above or below this number.

3. If the number obtained is between 1 and 10 use the "low half" of A (or R_1, $\sqrt{}$); if the number is between 10 and 100 use the "high half" of A (or R_2, $\sqrt{}$).

4. The correction number for the answer is one-half of the correction number noted in Step 2.

EXAMPLE 2.4C.   Calculate $(650)^{\frac{1}{2}}$.

$$\overset{+2}{Solution: (650)^{\frac{1}{2}} = (6.50)^{\frac{1}{2}}}$$

The setting for 6.50 is on the low half of A (or $\sqrt{}$ or R_1), and the resultant correction number is

$$\frac{1}{2}(+2) = +1$$

Thus

$$(650)^{\frac{1}{2}} = \overset{+2}{(6.50)^{\frac{1}{2}}} = \overset{+1}{2.55} = 25.5$$

EXAMPLE 2.4D.   Calculate $(0.000075)^{\frac{1}{4}}$.   The one-fourth power, or fourth root, may be found by taking the square root twice.

$$Solution: (0.000075)^{\frac{1}{4}} = \overset{-6}{(75)^{\frac{1}{4}}}$$

The resultant correction number for the first square root operation is

$$\frac{1}{2}(-6) = -3$$

and the setting is the same as for Example 2.4B.   Thus

$$\overset{-6}{(75)^{\frac{1}{2}}} = \overset{-3}{8.66} = 0.00866$$

Taking square root again

$$(0.00866)^{\frac{1}{2}} = \overset{-4}{(86.6)^{\frac{1}{2}}} =$$

The resultant correction number is

$$\frac{1}{2}(-4) = -2$$

and the setting is on the high half of A (or R, $\sqrt{}$), scale, or

$$(0.000075)^{\frac{1}{4}} \overset{-4}{=} (86.6)^{\frac{1}{2}} \overset{-2}{=} 9.3 = 0.093$$

EXAMPLE 2.4E. Calculate $\sqrt{0.0056}/\sqrt{140}$. This example may be solved by taking square roots of numerator and denominator, then their quotient. Generally it is faster to perform the division first, in effect writing

$$\frac{\sqrt{0.0056}}{\sqrt{140}} = \sqrt{\frac{0.0056}{140}} = \left(\underset{+2}{\overset{-4}{\frac{56}{1.40}}}\right)^{\frac{1}{2}} \overset{-6}{=} (40)^{\frac{1}{2}}$$

using a slide rule having A and B as well as C and D scales the fastest solution is: Calculate 56/1.40 by setting 1.40 on B (low half) to 56 on A (high half); the quotient appears on A at the left index of B; the square root is on D at the same index or

$$\overset{-6}{(40)^{\frac{1}{2}}} \overset{-3}{=} 6.32 = 0.00632$$

EXAMPLE 2.4F. Calculate $0.086^{-0.5}$. This represents $1/\sqrt{0.086}$. Therefore:

Set to 8.6 on B (low half)	Set the hairline to 8.6 on DI
$\sqrt{8.6}$ appears on C	$1/8.6$ appears on D
$1/\sqrt{8.6}$ may be read on CI as 0.341	$1/\sqrt{8.6}$ may be read on $\sqrt{}$ (high half)

The correction number of -2 in the denominator, upon taking square root becomes -1, and in the numerator $+1$. The decimal point position in the answer is 3.41.

If a pair of log scales with 2:1 cycle lengths is not available, it is possible to find square root by using a pair of log scales of equal cycle lengths. For example, the C and D scales, or CI and D scales, may be used. The method consists in finding, by trial, two equal numbers which multiplied together give the number for which the square root is desired.

EXAMPLE 2.4G. Calculate $\sqrt{33}$ using CI and D scales.

Solution:

Set the left index of CI to 33 on D
Move the hairline until the same setting is obtained on CI and D
(5.75)

If $\sqrt{3.3}$ were wanted, the right index of CI would be appropriate. The answer is 1.82.

2.5. Numerical Problems on Squares and Square Roots. For practical problems on squares and square roots applied to various fields of work, see Part II.

Perform the calculations indicated below.

	2A	2B	2C	2D
a	1.25^2	$\sqrt{0.165}$	0.275^2	$\sqrt{156}$
b	37.2^2	$\sqrt{2.70}$	176^2	$\sqrt{7.43}$
c	0.49^2	$\sqrt{437}$	4.52^2	$\sqrt{50.2}$
d	0.076^2	$\sqrt{39.5}$	76.2^2	$\sqrt{0.123}$
e	10.7^2	$\sqrt{0.00292}$	0.862^4	$\sqrt{0.236}$
f	825^2	$\sqrt{0.0185}$	89.4^2	$\sqrt{3765}$
g	9.05^2	$\sqrt{4.19}$	0.0152^2	$\sqrt{1085}$
h	146^2	$\sqrt{31.6}$	245^2	$\sqrt{334}$
i	0.392^2	$\sqrt{1230}$	36.1^2	$\sqrt{0.0059}$
j	87.5^2	$\sqrt{0.75}$	18.4^2	$\sqrt[4]{285}$
k	777^2	$\sqrt{92.5}$	0.0216^2	$\sqrt{111}$
l	0.0136^2	$\sqrt{1.8000}$	0.0037^2	$\sqrt{9.71}$
m	0.0028^2	$\sqrt{32.1}$	0.148^2	$\sqrt[8]{20.25}$
n	410^2	$\sqrt{7.08}$	392^2	$\sqrt{0.0196}$
o	25.7^2	$\sqrt{895}$	8.23^2	$\sqrt[4]{69,300}$
p	0.00175^2	$\sqrt{0.008}$	116^2	$\sqrt[8]{0.000378}$

2.6. Cubes. As described in Art. 2.1, the basic requirement for finding cubes and cube roots is a pair of related log scales on which the length of a cycle on one scale of the pair is three times as great as on the other. The 2:1 ratio test, described in Art. 1.4, may be used to identify logarithmic scales, and comparison of the lengths of a cycle on the scales will reveal those having a 3:1 ratio.

The general algebraic equation to be solved in finding either cubes or cube roots is

$$K_{\mathrm{K}} = M_{\mathrm{D}}{}^3; \frac{1}{3} \log K_{\mathrm{K}} = \log M_{\mathrm{D}} \tag{2.4}$$

The subscripts denote the slide rule scales constructed for these quantities on several of the commercial slide rules, Appendix pages 182–189. Therefore, to find the cube of a number using one of these slide rules:

Set the number, M, on D
Read the cube, K, on the K scale
See Fig. 2.14

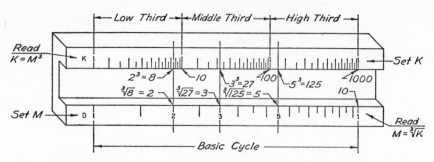

Fig. 2.14. Cubes of One-Digit Numbers on Non-Folded Scales

Set M on D: read $K = M^3$ on K
Examples: $2^3 = 8$; $3^3 = 27$; $5^3 = 125$

Certain slide rules, as noted in Art. 2.1, are based upon the slightly different form, that of Eq. (2.3)

$$\log K_D = 3 \log M \sqrt[3]{} \tag{2.3}$$

Thus, to find the cube of a number using this slide rule:

Set the number, M, on the $\sqrt[3]{}$ scale
Read the cube, K, on D
See Fig. 2.15

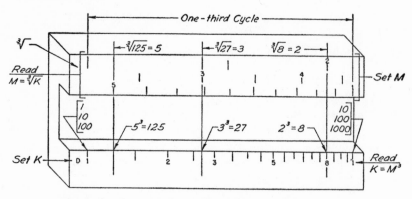

Fig. 2.15. Cubes of One-Digit Numbers on Folded Scales
Examples: $2^3 = 8$; $3^3 = 27$; $5^3 = 125$

A single statement of the method of operation which is applicable to all forms of slide rules is:

Set the number, M, on the expanded scale of the related pair of
logarithmic scales
Read the cube, K, on the compressed scale having a cycle length
one-third as great as the expanded scale

The decimal point position must be determined independently of the slide rule. The similar simple number scheme or the standard number method may be used. Both are illustrated by several examples.

EXAMPLE 2.6A. Calculate 16^3.

Solution:

Set glass to 16 on D   Set to 1.6 on $\sqrt[3]{}$ (low third)
Read 4.10 on K   Read 4.10 on D

For placing the decimal point, 16^3 is somewhat less than 20^3, which mentally is 8000; the answer therefore is 4100. Using standard numbers

$$\overset{+1}{16^3} = \overset{+3}{(1.6)^3} = 4.10 = 4100$$

EXAMPLE 2.6B. Calculate 0.045^3.

Solution:

Set to 4.5 on D   Set to 4.5 on $\sqrt[3]{}$ (middle third)
Read 91.0 on K   Read 91.0 on D

For placing the decimal point

$$\overset{-2}{0.045^3} = \overset{-6}{(4.5)^3} = 91.0 = 0.000091$$

Mentally, 4^3 is 64; and 4.5^3 is somewhat larger and is 91.

EXAMPLE 2.6C. Calculate 94^3.

Solution:

Set to 9.4 on D   Set to 9.4 on $\sqrt[3]{}$ (high third)
Read 830 on K   Read 830 on D

For placing the decimal point

$$100^3 = (10^2)^3 = (10)^6 = 1,000,000$$

and

$$94^3 = 830,000$$

EXAMPLE 2.6D. Calculate 1.06^6. This may be written $(1.06^3)^2$ or $(1.06^2)^3$. Choosing the first form the solution is:

Set the hairline to 1.06 on D   Set to 1.06 on $\sqrt[3]{}$ (low third)
Read the cube on K as 1.19   Read 1.19 on D
Set the hairline to 1.19 on D   Set to 1.19 on $\sqrt{}$ (low half)
Read the square on A as 1.42   Read 1.42 on D.

On the Versalog slide rule, Fig. A.7, set 1.06 on R_1; read 1.42 on K.

EXAMPLE 2.6E.   Calculate 0.0195^{-3}.   This represents $(1/0.0195)^3$.
Therefore, align the indices of CI with D and

Set to 0.0195 on CI	Set to 1.95 on $\sqrt[3]{}$
1/0.0195 appears on D	1.95^3 appears on D
Read 135 on K	$(1/1.95)^3$ may be read on DI

To place the decimal point: 1/0.02 is 50, and 50^3 is 125,000.   The answer
is 135,000.

Since to cube a number means to multiply it by itself three times, it is
apparent that another method for solving all of the problems of this article
is to use C and D scales, or D, CI, and C scales, as described for multiplication in Chapter 1.

2.7. Cube Roots.   The type form of equation

$$K = M^3; \log K = 3 \log M \qquad (2.3)$$

may be solved for K if M is known; this is the topic of Art. 2.6.   It may
be solved for M if K is known.   In this form one may write

$$\log M_D = \frac{1}{3} \log K_K \qquad (2.4)$$

It is a more laborious task to find cube root than it is square root by the
usual arithmetical methods.   Using the slide rule, a simple setting and
reading accomplishes the task.   However, care must be used to select the
correct section of the K or $\sqrt[3]{}$ scale depending upon the decimal point
position.

From the general theory of Art. 2.1, it may be observed that the
method of operation is:

> **Set the number, K, on the compressed scale of the related
>   pair of logarithmic scales**
> **Read its cube root, M, on the expanded scale (cycle length three
>   times that of the compressed scale)**

In specific terms applicable to the K and D scales:

> **Set the hairline to the number, K, on the K scale**
> **Read M, its cube root, on D**

Although all three cycles of K are sometimes numbered alike, it must
be observed that when taking cube roots of numbers between 1 and 1000,
the left cycle, or low third, of K represents numbers from 1 to 10; the

middle cycle represents numbers from 10 to 100; and the right cycle represents numbers from 100 to 1000 as shown in Fig. 2.14.

For the $\sqrt[3]{}$ scale the operating statement is:

Set the hairline to the number, K, on D
Read M, its cube root, on $\sqrt[3]{}$

Depending on decimal point position, the cube root is read on the low, middle, or high third of $\sqrt[3]{}$, Fig. 2.15.

EXAMPLE 2.7A. Calculate $\sqrt[3]{5}$.

Solution:

Set to 5 on the left cycle of K   Set to 5 on D
Read 1.71 on D   Read 1.71 on $\sqrt[3]{}$ (low third)

EXAMPLE 2.7B. Calculate $\sqrt[3]{250}$.

Solution:

Set to 250 on K (right)   Set to 250 on D
Read 6.3 on D   Read 6.3 on $\sqrt[3]{}$ (high third)

The correction number method provides a superior way for determining the portion of the scale to use for numbers outside of the range 1–1000.

1. Move the decimal point a multiple of three places to form a number between 1 and 1000.

2. Write the associated correction number above or below this number.

3. If the number obtained is between 1 and 10 use the "low third" of K (or $\sqrt[3]{}$); if the number is between 10 and 100 use the "middle third" of K (or $\sqrt[3]{}$); if the number is between 100 and 1000 use the "high third" of K (or $\sqrt[3]{}$).

4. The correction number of the answer is one-third of the correction number noted in Step 2.

EXAMPLE 2.7C. Calculate $\sqrt[3]{6330}$. *Solution:* Move the decimal point three places to the left, thus

$$\overset{+3}{\sqrt[3]{6330}} = (6.330)^{1/3}$$

The corrected number is found on the low third, and

$$\sqrt[3]{6.330} = 1.85; \overset{+1}{\sqrt[3]{6330}} = 1.85 = \mathbf{18.5}$$

EXAMPLE 2.7D.   Calculate $(0.0000393)^{1/3}$.

Solution: Moving the decimal point a multiple of three places to the right

$$(0.0000393)^{1/3} = (39.3)^{1/3} \overset{-6}{}$$

The number 39.3 is found on the middle third, and

$$(39.3)^{1/3} \overset{-6}{} = 3.4 \overset{-2}{} = 0.034$$

since

$$\frac{1}{3}(-6) = -2$$

EXAMPLE 2.7E.   Calculate $(2.62)^{-1/3}$. This represents $1/\sqrt[3]{2.62}$. Therefore, align the indices of CI with D and

Set to 2.62 on K (low third)   Set to 2.62 on DI
$\sqrt[3]{2.62}$ appears on D   1/2.62 appears on D
Read 0.726 on CI   Read $(1/2.62)^{1/3}$ on $\sqrt[3]{}$ (high
                                      third) as 0.726

If a pair of log scales with 3:1 cycle lengths is not available, it is possible to find cube root by a trial method similar to the trial method for finding square root described in Example 2.4G, page 66.

EXAMPLE 2.7F.   Calculate $\sqrt[3]{80}$ by trial.   *Solution:* Using D, CI, and C scales as described in Art. 1.18 multiply the three equal factors, trying successively:

$$4, 4.1, 4.2, 4.3, 4.4$$

Another trial or two will indicate that 4.31 is very close.   Certain of the suggested trial values could be skipped because their product is considerably smaller than 80.

If A, B, and D scales are available, a somewhat shorter method is:

Set the hairline to 80 on A (high half)
Move the slide until the same reading is found at the left index
  of C and beneath the hairline on B

Practically, it is seldom necessary to use this method, but an understanding of it is helpful.   The reader can test his understanding of the method by finding $\sqrt[3]{800}$ using A, B, and D scales.

2.8. Numerical Problems on Cubes and Cube Roots.   For practical problems on cubes and cube roots applied to various fields of work, see Part II.

Perform the calculations indicated below.

	2E	2F	2G	2H
a	$(2.42)^3$	$\sqrt[3]{1.08}$	$(7.25)^3$	$\sqrt[3]{8.27}$
b	$(4.65)^3$	$\sqrt[3]{21.3}$	$(18.7)^3$	$\sqrt[3]{78.5}$
c	$(0.112)^3$	$\sqrt[3]{175}$	$(0.832)^3$	$\sqrt[3]{490}$
d	$(276)^3$	$\sqrt[3]{840}$	$(48.5)^3$	$\sqrt[3]{1660}$
e	$(8.92)^3$	$\sqrt[3]{0.012}$	$(0.608)^3$	$\sqrt[3]{0.524}$
f	$(0.0316)^3$	$\sqrt[3]{0.0037}$	$(577)^3$	$\sqrt[3]{89.5}$
g	$(93.3)^3$	$\sqrt[3]{5265}$	$(6.43)^3$	$\sqrt[3]{0.0072}$
h	$(0.514)^3$	$\sqrt[3]{4,600,000}$	$(22.6)^3$	$\sqrt[3]{680,000}$
i	$(0.081)^3$	$\sqrt[3]{39,000}$	$(3.23)^3$	$\sqrt[3]{1960}$
j	$(190)^3$	$\sqrt[3]{0.555}$	$(0.021)^9$	$\sqrt[3]{24.5}$
k	$(108)^3$	$\sqrt[3]{69.5}$	$(12.4)^3$	$\sqrt[9]{875}$
l	$(20.4)^3$	$\sqrt[3]{0.0029}$	$(27.8)^3$	$\sqrt[3]{0.032}$
m	$(4.61)^3$	$\sqrt[3]{0.098}$	$(29.2)^6$	$\sqrt[3]{157}$
n	$(1.025)^3$	$\sqrt[3]{93.8}$	$(0.792)^3$	$\sqrt[6]{37.8}$
o	$(2.38)^3$	$\sqrt[3]{17.3}$	$(0.518)^3$	$\sqrt[3]{0.00027}$
p	$(0.045)^3$	$\sqrt[3]{48,700}$	$(1.51)^9$	$\sqrt[9]{0.826}$

2.9. Other Simple Powers and Roots. A number may be squared twice to obtain its fourth power. If a number is cubed, then squared, its sixth power will be obtained as shown in Example 2.6D, page 69. In a similar manner other whole number multiples of 2 and 3 as powers or roots may be obtained.

Certain fractional powers also may be obtained using the cube and square scales together. Thus, one may solve for P or R in the equation

$$P = R^{3/2}; \text{ or } P^{1/3} = R^{1/2} \tag{2.5}$$

In logarithmic form

$$\frac{1}{3} \log P_\mathrm{K} = \frac{1}{2} \log R_\mathrm{A} \tag{2.6}$$

With reference to the particular slide rules discussed here, since the scale factor, or length of one cycle on A is one-half as much as the length on C or D scale, and one cycle on K is one-third as long as the D scale, if R is set on the A scale, P may be read on K.

Eq. (2.6) may be written

$$2 \log P_{\sqrt{\ }} = 3 \log R_{\sqrt[3]{\ }} \tag{2.7}$$

In this form, the setting on $\sqrt{\ }$ and $\sqrt[3]{\ }$ scales is indicated. Since the coefficient of log P is 2 and the $\sqrt{\ }$ scale is twice as long as C or D, P is found on $\sqrt{\ }$; the $\sqrt[3]{\ }$ scale is three times as long as the C or D scale, hence log R with coefficient 3 is found on $\sqrt[3]{\ }$.

As another method of analysis, a number set on A would have its square root on D; and the cube of the number on D appears on the K scale.   Or

$$P = (R^{1/2})^3 = R^{3/2} \qquad (2.5)$$

Of course squares and cubes of 3/2 powers may be obtained by methods of Arts. 2.3 and 2.6.   Although 9/4, 27/8, and other such powers of numbers are seldom wanted, the possibility of obtaining them by raising to the 3/2 power a second and third time is worth noting for its relationship to general slide rule principles.

Of course Eq. (2.5) may be written

$$R = P^{2/3} \qquad (2.8)$$

and this may be solved for R on the particular slide rules as follows:

Set the hairline to P on K   Set the hairline to P on $\sqrt{}$
$P^{1/3}$ appears on D P^2 appears on D
Read $R = (P^{1/3})^2$ on A   Read $R = (P^2)^{1/3}$ on $\sqrt[3]{}$

The decimal point position is sometimes troublesome in these fractional power problems, but Fig. 2.16 should be helpful.   For several of the following examples the decimal point position is completely worked out.

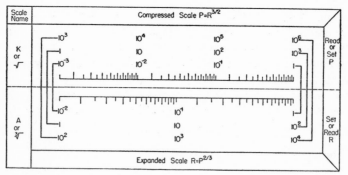

Fig. 2.16.   Diagram of Operation and Decimal Point Location for 3/2 and 2/3 Powers

EXAMPLE 2.9A.   Calculate $3.3^{3/2}$.

Solution:

Set the hairline to 3.3 on A   Set the hairline to 3.3 on $\sqrt[3]{}$
$3.3^{1/2}$ appears on D (less than 2) 3.3^3 appears on D (as 36)
$(3.3^{1/2})^3$ appears on K as 6.00 $\sqrt{3.3^3}$ appears on $\sqrt{}$ as 6.00

EXAMPLE 2.9B.   Calculate $0.15^{3/2}$.   *Solution:* Move the decimal point a multiple of two places to form a number between 1 and 100, then

Set the hairline to 15 on A (high half)
$\sqrt{15}$ appears on D (as 3.87)
3.87^3 appears on K, as 58.0

or

$$(0.15)^{\frac{3}{2}} \overset{-2}{=} (15)^{\frac{3}{2}} \overset{-1}{=} (3.87)^3 \overset{-3}{=} 58 = 0.058$$

The 3.87 need not be read and one may place the decimal point in the 58 read from the slide rule by observing that $15^{\frac{3}{2}}$ is greater than 15 and less than 225, which is the value of 15^2. The correction number is

$$\frac{3}{2}(-2) = -3$$

Using $\sqrt{}$ and $\sqrt[3]{}$ scales

Set (0.15) or (1.5) $\overset{-1}{}$ on $\sqrt[3]{}$ (low third)

$(1.5)^3$ $\overset{-1}{}$ appears on D $\overset{-3}{}$ (as 3.38)

$3.38 \overset{-3}{=} 33.8; \overset{-4}{(33.8)^{\frac{1}{2}}} \overset{-4}{=} 5.8 \overset{-2}{}$

$(33.8)^{\frac{1}{2}}$ $\overset{-4}{}$ is read on $\sqrt{}$ (high half)

EXAMPLE 2.9C. Calculate $465^{\frac{2}{3}}$.

Solution:

Set to 465 on K (high third)   Set to 4.65 $\overset{+2}{}$ on $\sqrt{}$ (low half)

$465^{\frac{1}{3}}$ appears on D (nearly 8) $(4.65)^2$ $\overset{+2}{}$ is on D $\overset{+4}{}$ (as 21.6, $\overset{+3}{}$ or 216)

$(465^{\frac{1}{3}})^2$ appears on A as 60 $(216)^{\frac{1}{3}} \overset{+3}{=} 6.0 \overset{+1}{=} 60$ appears on $\sqrt[3]{}$ (low third)

Another way for placing the decimal point is: $400^{\frac{1}{2}}$ is 20; therefore, $465^{\frac{1}{2}}$ is greater than 20, and $465^{\frac{2}{3}}$ is greater than 20 and less than 465.

EXAMPLE 2.9D. Calculate $5600^{\frac{2}{3}}$.

Solution:

Set to 5.600 $\overset{+3}{}$ on K (low third)   Set the hairline to 5.600 $\overset{+3}{}$ on $\sqrt{}$

$(5.600)^{\frac{1}{3}}$ $\overset{+3}{}$ appears on D $\overset{+1}{}$ (as 1.78) $(5.600)^2$ $\overset{+3}{}$ appears on D $\overset{+6}{}$ (as 31.6)

On A $(1.78)^2 \overset{+1}{=} 3.15 \overset{+2}{=} 315$ On $\sqrt[3]{}$ (middle) read $(31.6)^{\frac{1}{3}}$ $\overset{+6}{}$ as 3.15 $\overset{+2}{}$

EXAMPLE 2.9E. Calculate $30,000^{\frac{4}{5}}$.

Solution: Set the hairline to 30.0 on K (middle third)

$$\overset{+3}{(30.0)^{1/3}} \text{ appears on D (as } \overset{+1}{3.11})$$

$$\text{On A the } \overset{+1}{(3.11)^2} \text{ is read as } \overset{+2}{9.67} \text{ for } 30{,}000^{2/3}.$$

This intermediate result on A must be squared to obtain the 4/3 power, or using A and B scales, for example

$$\overset{+2}{9.67} \times \overset{+2}{9.67} = \overset{+4}{93.4} = 934{,}000$$

Another method by which it may be easier to determine the decimal point position is as follows:

$$30{,}000^{4/3} = 30{,}000^{1+\frac{1}{3}} = 30{,}000 \ \sqrt[3]{30{,}000}$$
$$= 30{,}000 \times 31.1^{+} = 934{,}000$$

EXAMPLE 2.9F. Calculate $(0.275)^{-2/3}$. This represents $1/(0.275)^{2/3}$. To solve this with one setting, a slide rule is required which has an inverted scale associated with the scale on which the setting is made, or associated with the answer. The particular commercial slide rules shown in the Appendix do not have an inverted scale associated with any one of the scales A, K, $\sqrt{\ }$, $\sqrt[3]{\ }$, or R. Therefore, the problem may be solved by finding $0.275^{2/3}$ and then taking the reciprocal in a separate operation. Thus,

$$0.275^{2/3} = 0.422; \ 1/0.275^{2/3} = 2.36$$

It would be possible to construct a pair of log scales having many other ratios of cycle lengths, representing other powers of numbers. In fact, charts of this nature for a number of different powers have been published.[1]

2.10. Equations Containing Simple Powers or Roots. The preceding example is one which may be solved more rapidly with LogLog scales. In fact, it is possible to solve all of the examples of this chapter by using LogLog scales along with C, CI, and D scales, as described in Chapter 4. However, for some problems the accuracy attainable with the LogLog scales is less than it is with the square and cube scales. Further, certain common equations containing simple powers and roots with coefficients are not as simply solved by LogLog scales. If the LogLog scales are used for these equations it may be necessary to read and re-set on different scales for several distinct operations.

It will be observed that the previous examples in this chapter, with very few exceptions, are solved by mechanically equating lengths on two log scales of cycle lengths appropriately related for the exponent involved.

---

[1] Kulmann, C. Albert, *Nomographic Charts*, pages 4–27. New York: McGraw Hill, 1951.

The examples in this article are slightly more complex in that addition or subtraction of lengths is also used. That is, these examples require division or multiplication along with simple powers or roots.

The solutions described with these examples are the ones requiring minimum slide rule manipulation and which, if possible, avoid reading on one scale and re-setting that quantity on another scale in order to complete the calculation. This minimum setting for certain examples is possible on only one, or perhaps two, of the commercial slide rules shown in the Appendix. The technique of selecting a procedure which will lead to minimum settings is difficult to express in general terms.[2] Essentially, it is to anticipate the scales which will be used for the power or root operation; then carry out the divisions or multiplications on scales which will make reading and re-setting unnecessary. For some of the simpler problems the reader might profitably attempt a minimum setting with his slide rule before examining the solution given.

If one is to be proficient with the slide rule, facility in solving some of these equations is desirable. Others, which arise infrequently in the application of the slide rule, are included primarily for reference. If a series of quadratic equations with varying coefficients is to be solved with the slide rule, for example, reference to this section and Example 2.10K should be helpful. If, on the other hand, a single quadratic equation is to be solved, a short method of solution is unimportant.

EXAMPLE 2.10A. Calculate $x = \dfrac{15.6 \sqrt{7}}{19.2}$. *Solution:* If $\sqrt{7}$ is found first by a method which will set it on D, the remaining calculations may be carried through in one setting of the slide by using the C and D scales for the continued division and multiplication. The method is

Set the hairline to 7 on A (low half)
$\sqrt{7}$ appears on D (2.64 approx.)
Place 19.2 on C beneath the hairline
At 15.6 on C read 2.15 on D

EXAMPLE 2.10B. Calculate $x = \dfrac{7.1}{8.4} \sqrt[3]{85}$. *Solution:* The reasoning is the same as for Example 2.10A, and the form is similar, but it is a cube root rather than a square root which is to be obtained first. Thus

Set the hairline to 85 on K (middle third)
$\sqrt[3]{85}$ appears on D (as 4.4)
Place 8.4 on C beneath the hairline
At 7.1 on C read 3.72 on D

---

[2] A large number of slide rule settings for special formulas using certain commercial slide rules are tabulated in Thompson, J. E., *A Manual of the Slide Rule*, pages 171–203. New York: D. Van Nostrand Co., 1930.

EXAMPLE 2.10C.   Calculate $x = 2.1\sqrt{\dfrac{42 \times 18.5}{68}}$.   *Solution:* If the
operations under the radical are performed using A and B scales, the
result may appear on A, and its square root on D; multiplication by 2.1
then can be performed using C and D scales without reading intermediate
partial answers.

> Set the hairline to 42 on A(high half)
> Place 68 on B(high half) beneath the hairline
> Move the hairline to 18.5 on B(high half)
> Partial answer is on A beneath the hairline
> Square root of partial answer is on D beneath the hairline
>   (3.4 approx.)
> Multiplication by 2.1 yields 7.10

The decimal point position for the quantity under the radical must be
carefully observed.   It is very easy to obtain the partial answer on the
incorrect half of A, then the square root is incorrect in the ratio of $\sqrt{10}:1$,
or 3.16:1.

If the foregoing three examples are solved on a slide rule having $\sqrt[3]{}$
and $\sqrt{}$ or R scales, Figs. A.5 and A.7, pages 186, and 188, additional
operations are required.   The quantity, $\sqrt{7}$, for example, is found on
$\sqrt{}$ or R scale and must be read and re-set on D to complete the solution.

On the other hand, Example 2.10G can be solved with fewer operations
on a slide rule having $\sqrt[3]{}$ scales instead of a K scale.

EXAMPLE 2.10D.   Calculate $x = \dfrac{69 \times 4.2^2}{8.5}$.   *Solution:* For two of the
commercial slide rules pictured in the Appendix, squares may be read
on the D scale; the other squares are read on the A scale.   The two
operating statements for the shortest setting are

> Set the hairline to 4.2 on D
> 4.2^2 appears on A beneath the hairline
> Set 8.5 on B beneath the hairline
> At 69 on B read 143 on A

or

> Set the hairline to 4.2 on $\sqrt{}$ (or R_2)
> 4.2^2 appears on D beneath the hairline
> Set 8.5 on C beneath the hairline
> At 69 on C read 143 on D

EXAMPLE 2.10E.   Calculate the circle areas: $\dfrac{\pi}{4}3.5^2$; $\dfrac{\pi}{4}4.4^2$; $\dfrac{\pi}{4}5.3^2$.

Solution: These are similar in form to the preceding example.

However, the simplest method of operation, because of the $\pi/4$ in all of the problems, is

Set the right index of B to $\pi/4$ (or 0.7854) on A
Move the hairline successively on C to 3.5, 4.4, 5.3
Read the several answers on A beneath the hairline

or

Set the right index of C to 4 on D
Move the hairline to the successive diameters on $\sqrt{}$ (or R)
Read the several answers on CF

The latter method may be analyzed as follows:

If d is on $\sqrt{}$ (or R) scale
d^2 appears on the D scale, and
πd^2 appears on DF

Adjust the CF scale so the readings on CF will be one-fourth of the aligned DF reading.

EXAMPLE 2.10F.   Calculate the circle areas: $\pi 7.6^2$; $\pi 8.7^2$; $\pi 9.8^2$; $\pi 10.9^2$. *Solution:* This is like the preceding example in form, but with a coefficient of π instead of $\pi/4$.   One method is:

Set successive values of radius, r, on $\sqrt{}$ or R scale
r^2 appears on D
πr^2 appears on DF

EXAMPLE 2.10G.   Calculate $x = \dfrac{6.7 \times 4.3^3}{8.2}$.

Solution: Set the hairline to 4.3 on $\sqrt[3]{}$
$\qquad$ 4.3^3 appears beneath the hairline on D (approx. 80)

Using the C and D scales to complete the division and multiplication:

Place 8.2 on C beneath the hairline
At 6.7 on C read $x = 65.0$

If 4.3 is cubed using a K scale, the result must be read and re-set on D for carrying out the division and multiplication.   It is easily done, but requires a reading and setting operation not needed with the $\sqrt[3]{}$ scale.

EXAMPLE   2.10H.   Calculate $x = 1.6\left(\dfrac{5.4 \times 18}{2.05}\right)^2$.   *Solution:* The division and multiplication in parentheses can be performed using C and D scales; the answer will appear on D (as 47.5), and its square will be on A; multiplication by 1.6 can be performed with A and B scales.   Or, by reading the partial answer one may note that it reduces to

$$x = 1.6 \times 47.5^2 = 1.6 \times 47.5 \times 47.5$$

This may be performed simply by using CI, C and D scales as in Example 1.18D, page 40.

EXAMPLE 2.10I.   Calculate $x = \dfrac{9.1 \times 4.5^{\frac{2}{3}}}{17.2}$.

Solution: Set the hairline to 4.5 on K (low third)
         $4.5^{\frac{1}{3}}$ appears on D beneath the hairline
         $(4.5^{\frac{1}{3}})^2$ appears on A beneath the hairline
         Set 17.2 on B beneath the hairline
         At 9.1 on B, read $x = 1.44$ on A

If K, A, and B scales are not found on the slide rule being used, intermediate reading and setting of partial solution is necessary.

EXAMPLE 2.10J.   Calculate $x = 5.2\left(\dfrac{7.6 \times 5.9}{18.6}\right)^{\frac{2}{3}}$.   *Solution:* If one had a slide rule with K scale on both frame and slide, intermediate reading of partial answer for this problem would not be necessary. None of the commercial slide rules, Figs. A.1 to A.8, of the Appendix is made with moving and stationary K scale, so using any one of these slide rules it is necessary to calculate and read $7.6 \times 5.9/18.6$ first.

EXAMPLE 2.10K.   Calculate $x = \sqrt{17.5^2 + 4.2^2}$.   Problems of this nature occur in slide rule applications much more frequently than some of the other examples in this article.   Hence, skill in solving problems of this type is important.   One obvious method for solving this example is

       Set 17.5 on D; read 17.5^2 on A as 306
       Set 4.2 on D; read 4.2^2 on A as 17.6
       Mentally add: $306 + 17.6 = 323.6$
       Set 323.6 on A; read $\sqrt{323.6}$ on D as 18.0

The $\sqrt{}$ or R scales also may be used in similar manner. However, in problems such as this in which one of the numbers (4.2) is less than one-fourth of the other, (17.5), a simpler, as well as more accurate, slide rule result is obtained by an approximation:

$$x = 17.5 + \frac{4.2^2}{2 \times 17.5}$$

In algebraic terms, to solve

$$x = \sqrt{a^2 + b^2}$$

the series approximation

$$x = a + \frac{b^2}{2a} \qquad (4b < a) \tag{2.9}$$

gives accurate results under the limitation, b less than one-fourth of a. Only the second term, $b^2/2a$, requires slide rule operation, and for the numerical example

$$x = 17.5 + 0.504 = 18.004$$

As an indication of the accuracy of the series approximation, the error of the method for several ratios is:

Ratio	Approximation Error in x	
a/b	Per cent	One part per:
5	0.019	5200
4	0.046	2180
3.5	0.076	1320
3	0.139	720
2.5	0.276	360

EXAMPLE 2.10L. Calculate $x = \sqrt{9.6^2 - 2.2^2}$. This example may be solved by the same kind of series approximation as the preceding one. Thus

$$x = 9.6 - \frac{2.2^2}{2 \times 9.6} \qquad \text{(approx.)}$$

In algebraic terms

$$x = \sqrt{a^2 - b^2} = a - \frac{b^2}{2a} \qquad (4b < a) \tag{2.10}$$

The theoretical error of using this approximation for a/b of 4 is slightly greater, but negligibly so for slide rule work. It is one part in 1920, instead of 1 part in 2180, for Example 2.10K. For b progressively smaller than one-fourth of a, the theoretical error declines rapidly, so that if b is $0.1a$, the approximation formula will give better than slide rule reading accuracy.

EXAMPLE 2.10M. Find the roots of the equation: $x^2 + 5.4x = 7.1$. Quadratic equations such as this can be solved by trial, aided by a slide rule. It is helpful to divide by x, then $x + 5.4 = 7.1/x$. The CI and D scales can be used to solve the quantity $7.1/x$ in one slide setting for various trial values of x.

Solution: Set the right index of CI to 7.1 on D
Move the hairline to successive trial values of x on CI: 2, 1.5, 1.2, etc.
Read $7.1/x$ on D
See Fig. 2.17 for final setting

As preliminary trial values, 1 and 2 might be selected. It is then evident that a root lies between these numbers. The product of the two roots is the term 7.1. Therefore, the final hairline position marks one root on CI and the other on D. In this example, both roots are positive and the coefficients are positive in the form the equation is written. Negative coefficients or negative roots are as readily solvable, except for requiring care with signs.

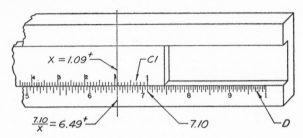

Fig. 2.17. Solution of Quadratic Equation

Example: 2.10M; $x + 5.4 = 7.1/x$; $1.09 + 5.4 = 6.49$

EXAMPLE 2.10N. Find the roots of the equation $x^3 - 47x - 38 = 0$. If the equation is written

$$x^2 - 47 - \frac{38}{x} = 0$$

successive values of x may be tried to obtain the roots. For example, if 8 and 7 are tried, the remainder is not zero, but changes sign between the two. Several trials will lead to 7.24 as one root. In a similar way, other roots of -6.42 and -0.82 may be found.

On certain commercial slide rules it is possible to make a single setting and read both $38/x$ and x^2.

A slide rule is not a great deal of help in solving cubic equations, but does aid in trial calculation methods.

2.11. Summary, Chapter 2. 1. *General Form.* The logarithmic scales discussed in this chapter permit the solution with one setting, by equating lengths on appropriate slide rule scales, of the general algebraic equation

$$x_1^a = x_2^b; \text{ or } x_1 = x_2^{b/a}$$

or in logarithmic form

$$\log x_1 = (b/a)(\log x_2) \tag{2.11}$$

for values of b/a of 3/2, or 2, or 3, or reciprocals of these. Sums, differences, or products of these numbers as exponents may be calculated by reading intermediate answers and re-setting (Example 2.6D). The LogLog scales discussed in Chapter 4 are useful in solving Eq. (2.11) for b/a having any value.

It would be possible to devise a pair of related logarithmic scales to solve Eq. (2.11) for any desired value of b/a, but because of limited usefulness compared to squares and cubes the general purpose slide rules include only 2:1 and 3:1 log scales.

2. *Commercial Slide Rules.* Each of the commercial slide rules shown in the Appendix, Figs. A.1 to A.8, has two log scales in addition to the basic C and D scales. There are four different lengths represented, however. In terms of the basic D, the scale equations are:

$$\frac{1}{2} \log x_A \qquad \frac{1}{3} \log x_K$$

$$2 \log x_R, \sqrt{} \qquad 3 \log x \sqrt[3]{}$$

$$\log x_D$$

Thus to find the equation solved by equating lengths on a pair of these scales, one may equate the appropriate terms above and transform the equation. For example, the A and D scales solve

$$\frac{1}{2} \log x_A = \log x_D$$

which is

$$x_A^{1/2} = x_D; \text{ or } x_A = x_D^2$$

Similarly, for $\sqrt{}$ and $\sqrt[3]{}$ scales

$$2 \log x\sqrt{} = 3 \log x\sqrt[3]{}$$

3. *Decimal Point Position.* Mental approximation with given numbers rounded off to one digit and zeros is a satisfactory method for placing the decimal point in squares or cubes of numbers, Example 2.6C, page 69. The standard number method is helpful for very large or very small numbers, (Art. 2.6). For example

$$\overset{+3}{6000^2} = (\overset{+3}{6.0})^2 = \overset{+3}{6.0} \times \overset{+6}{6.0} = 36.0 = 36 \times 10^6$$

and

$$\overset{-2}{0.04^3} = (\overset{-2}{4.0})^3 = \overset{-2}{4} \times \overset{-2}{4} \times \overset{-6}{4} = 64 = 0.000064$$

The correction number method is by far the most satisfactory plan for finding square roots or cube roots of numbers whose answers lie outside the primary cycle range. This method more clearly shows the scale cycle on which to set or read, as well as indicating the decimal point position.

The correction number method may be described in general terms as follows. If 10^m or 10^{-m}, m being an integer, is factored out of a number whose mth root is to be found, then

$$\sqrt[m]{10^m P} = 10 \sqrt[m]{P}; \text{ and } \sqrt[m]{10^{-m} P} = 0.1 \sqrt[m]{P}$$

Factoring 10^m one, two, or three times thus has the effect of a decimal point shift of one, two, or three places, respectively.

The worked out examples of this chapter are only for m of 2 or 3 and 10^m of 100 or 1000.   Other values of m are possible; on the Versalog slide rule, Fig. A.7, page 188, for the K and R scales m would be 6.   For this pair the decimal point would be moved a multiple of 6 places to obtain a number between 1 and 1,000,000, then set on the correct cycle of K, and so on.

4. *Solution of Equations.*   (Art. 2.10)   Quadratic equations and equations containing other powers often can be solved by trial for real roots using the slide rule (Examples 2.10M, 2.10N).   In many practical calculation problems, one positive root only is sought.

A direct method for performing divisions and multiplications along with simple powers, and without reading intermediate values, is sometimes possible.   This requires anticipating the scales on which a root or power will be found, and performing divisions or multiplications with the scales and in the sequence which coordinates with the root or power operation.   The Examples 2.10A to 2.10L illustrate the method.

2.12. Problems on Chapter 2.   Perform the calculations indicated below.

Solve the following:

	2I	2J	2K
a	$\sqrt{16^2 + 3.5^2}$	$\sqrt{0.65^2 + 2.8^2}$	$\sqrt{48^2 + 10.8^2}$
b	$\sqrt{0.192^2 + 0.042^2}$	$\sqrt{7.8^2 + 0.62^2}$	$\sqrt{420^2 + 1820^2}$
c	$\sqrt{0.27^2 + 1.85^2}$	$\sqrt{0.35^2 + 0.18^2}$	$\sqrt{0.96^2 + 0.72^2}$
d	$\sqrt{32^2 + 2.6^2}$	$\sqrt{22^2 + 9.5^2}$	$\sqrt{0.067^2 + 0.31^2}$
e	$\sqrt{20^2 - 4.2^2}$	$\sqrt{76^2 - 15^2}$	$\sqrt{0.93^2 - 0.56^2}$
f	$\sqrt{0.18^2 - 0.036^2}$	$\sqrt{0.071^2 - 0.035^2}$	$\sqrt{450^2 - 95^2}$
g	$\sqrt{756^2 - 340^2}$	$\sqrt{0.46^2 - 0.082^2}$	$\sqrt{1.27^2 - 0.71^2}$
h	$\sqrt{0.44^2 - 0.102^2}$	$\sqrt{8.12^2 - 1.7^2}$	$\sqrt{0.54^2 - 0.13^2}$

Find one or more roots for each of the following:

i $x^2 - 56x = 17.5$	$3x^2 - 7.5x = -2.7$	$x^3 - 62x = -120$
j $x^2 + 8.9x = -10.5$	$5.2x^2 - 17.6x = 15$	$x^3 - 2.4x = 1.52$
k $x^2 - 3.7x = 4.8$	$x^2 + 8.8x = -2.9$	$x^3 - 7.2x = 6.5$
l $x^2 - 20x = 63$	$1.7x^2 - 32x = 25$	$x^3 - 0.5x = 0.15$

Solve the following with minimum possible number of settings.

m $\dfrac{256\sqrt{8.2}}{18}$	$\sqrt{\dfrac{7.5 \times 3.8}{0.13}}$	$\dfrac{76.5}{\sqrt{18 \times 31}}$
n $\dfrac{19.2\sqrt{43}}{0.73}$	$\sqrt{\dfrac{0.96 \times 0.41}{72}}$	$\dfrac{15.2 \times 12.8}{\sqrt{14.9}}$

	2I	2J	2K

o $\dfrac{127 \sqrt[3]{760}}{0.91}$ $\sqrt{\dfrac{746}{21\pi}}$ $\left(\dfrac{315 \times 16}{215}\right)^{\frac{2}{3}}$

p $\dfrac{82.8 \sqrt[3]{0.037}}{0.017}$ $\sqrt{\dfrac{0.013 \times 25}{42.2}}$ $\left(\dfrac{123}{0.51 \times 0.73}\right)^{\frac{2}{3}}$

2L

Calculate and prepare a graph for each of the following:

a The force of wind on a rectangular surface is given by the equation: $F = 0.004AV^2$ where F = force in lbs; A = area in square feet; V = wind velocity in mph, 0 to 60. Select one or two different values for A.

b The force of wind on a cylindrical surface is given by the equation: $F = 0.0025DV^2$ where F = force in lb per foot of length; D = diameter in ft; V = wind velocity in mph, 0 to 60. Select one or two different values for D.

c The power required to drive a particular ventilating fan is given by the equation: $P = 1.25 \times 10^{-7}S^3$ where S = speed in rpm, 0 to 1200; P = power in hp.

d The volume of a cylindrical tank is given by this equation: $V = \dfrac{1728\pi}{924} D^2H$ where D = diameter in ft, 0 to 10; H = height in ft, 1 ft; V = gallons.

e The Francis' weir formula is: $Q = 3.33bH^{\frac{3}{2}}$ where b = width of weir, 10 ft; H = head of water, 0 to 1.5 ft; Q = discharge in cfs.

f The period of pendulum is given by: $T = 2\pi \sqrt{\dfrac{L}{g}}$ where T = period of pendulum in sec; L = length of pendulum, ft, 1 to 6; g = acceleration of gravity, 32.2 ft./sec.^{2}

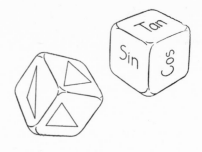

Chapter

3

TRIGONOMETRIC FUNCTIONS

AND CALCULATIONS

3.1. Principle and Arrangement of Trigonometric Scales. As shown in Chapter 1, the cyclic nature of the log scale permits multiplications and divisions with "slide rule accuracy" for any numbers, large or small, if the decimal point position is determined separately. In Chapter 2, for simple powers and roots, the decimal point position for numbers on the expanded scale of a pair may be shifted at will, Figs. 2.12 and 2.13, page 64.

The trigonometric functions and the slide rule scales for them are cyclic, but not on a decimal basis. That is, tan 70° is not 10 times tan 7°, for example. Two important negative characteristics of the trigonometric slide rule scales result from this non-decimal property.

1. The angle value marked on the scales cannot be extended by changing the decimal point position.
2. Trigonometric functions for all possible angle values cannot be read from the slide rule.

Thus, the tangent scale on some commercial slide rules ranges only from 5°43′ or 5.71° to 45°.

Although at first glance this appears to be a serious limitation of the usefulness of the slide rule for trigonometry, it is possible, by making use of trigonometric properties and relationships, to read directly from the slide rule the tangent or any other of the six trigonometric functions over a much wider range than 5° to 45°. Mechanically, the method of operation for reading trigonometric functions is to equate lengths on the appropriate scales in the same manner as for the simple powers and roots of Chapter 2.

If triangles are to be solved with the slide rule, operations of division or multiplication are required along with the setting for sine, tangent, or other function.   Thus, the solution of triangles requires addition or subtraction of logarithmic lengths along with the trigonometric scale setting.

Many variations in slide rule design have been made with regard to the placing and association of the trigonometric scales.   For example, the trigonometric scales may be found on the frame or on the slide, or on both. Slide rules have been made on which the trigonometric scales were associated with the B scale, or with the C scale; or, a sine scale may go with B and a tangent scale with the C scale.   On some slide rules the trigonometric scales increase to the left; on others, they increase to the right.

The commercial slide rules shown in the Appendix, Figs. A.1 to A.8, have been selected partly because of the variations in the trigonometric scales.   Although not shown, a sine and tangent scale are found on the back of the slide in Fig. A.1.   Several of these slide rules have scales graduated in degrees and minutes; most are in degrees and decimal parts of degrees.   On Fig. A.2 the sine scale is associated with the B scale and the tangent scale goes with C.   On Fig. A.8 the trigonometric scales are on the frame; the other slide rules have these scales on the slide.

In general mathematical terms, if

$$x = \sin A$$

then

$$\log x_\mathrm{C} = \log \sin A_\mathrm{S} \tag{3.1}$$

and if

$$y = \tan A$$

then

$$\log y_\mathrm{C} = \log \tan A_\mathrm{T} \tag{3.2}$$

Eq. (3.1) and (3.2) are the forms of trigonometric scales for most of the commercial slide rules shown in the Appendix, Figs. A.1 to A.8, the subscripts denoting the names of the scales on which reading or setting is made.

If one wishes to determine for an unfamiliar slide rule the appropriate scales on which to read sine or tangent, a variation of the 2:1 ratio test described in Chapter 1 is helpful.   Since sin 30° is 0.5 and sin 90° is 1.0, the logarithmic scale on which 0.5 matches a 30° graduation and 1.0 matches with 90° will determine the pair of scales to use for sines.   Also, since tan 26.5° is slightly less than 0.5 and tan 45° is 1.0, the pair of scales for tangents may be found by a similar method.

3.2. Graduation of Scales. The plan of subdivision of trigonometric scales depends upon their length, and also upon whether angles are divided into decimal parts of a degree or into degrees and minutes.

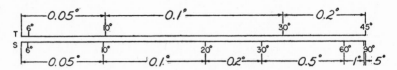

Fig. 3.1. Diagram of Finest Graduation Intervals and Scale Limits on **10-Inch** Trigonometric Scales, Decimally Divided

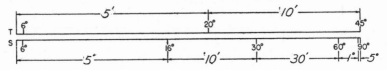

Fig. 3.2. Diagram of Finest Graduation Intervals and Scale Limits on **10-Inch** Trigonometric Scales, Divided Into Minutes

Figs. 3.1 and 3.2 indicate in diagrammatic form the usual plan for subdividing these scales for 10-inch slide rules on which the trigonometric scales are associated with the C and D scales.

As a matter of convenience the examples are worked out in decimal parts of degrees. Some of the problems and some of the answers are in minutes and seconds for parts of degrees.

3.3. Sines. The subscripts in Eq. (3.1) indicate that the operating procedure for obtaining the sine of an angle is:

Set the hairline to the angle, A, on the S scale
Read sin A on the C scale beneath the hairline

Several examples illustrate the setting and the placing of the decimal point.

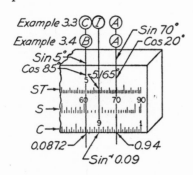

Fig. 3.3. Scale Settings for Sines and Cosines

Examples: 3.3A:sin 70°; 3.3C:sin 5°; 3.3I: sin⁻¹0.09; 3.4A: cos 20°; 3.4B: cos 85°

EXAMPLE 3.3A.   Find sin 70°.

Solution: Set hairline to 70° on S
Read 9.4 on the C scales

The sine never exceeds 1.0, which is the value of sin 90°.   Sin 70°, there-fore, is 0.94.   See Fig. 3.3.   Some slide rules have the complementary angle values also marked on the S scale.   These are omitted from Fig. 3.3.

EXAMPLE 3.3B.   Find sin 7°.

Solution: Set the hairline to 7° on S
Read 0.122 on the C scale, Fig. 3.4

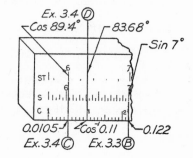

Fig. 3.4. Scale Settings for Sines and Cosines

Examples: 3.3B:sin 7°; 3.4C:cos 89.4°;
3.4D:cos^{-1} 0.11

EXAMPLE 3.3C.   Find sin 5°.

Solution: Set the hairline to 5° on ST
Read 0.0872 on the C scale, Fig. 3.3

As noted on Fig. 3.1, the S scale includes angles whose sines lie between 0.1 and 1.0; the ST scale includes angles whose sines lie between 0.01 and 0.1.   For angles smaller than 0.57°, or 0°34′, and having sines less than 0.01, the sine cannot be read from the slide rule, but the sine of a small angle can be found from the approximation

$$\sin A° = \frac{\pi}{180} A° \quad \text{(for small } A \text{; 3° or less)}$$

$$= 0.01745A° \tag{3.3}$$

EXAMPLE 3.3D.   Find sin 0°27′.   *Solution:* The angle expressed in degrees is 27/60, hence from Eq. (3.3)

$$\sin 0°27′ = \frac{27}{60} \times 0.01745 = 0.00785$$

Several of the commercial slide rules have gauge marks useful for finding sines of small angles if the angle is expressed in minutes or seconds. A mark (′) to the left of 2° on the S scale, or it may be on the C scale at 3.44, identifies the minutes gauge mark.

Set the hairline to angle in minutes on D
Set (') beneath the hairline
At the index of C read sine on D

The seconds gauge mark ('') near 1.5° is similarly used for small angles in seconds.

EXAMPLE 3.3E.   Find sin 127°.   *Solution:* The S scale is marked only with angles up to 90°, therefore, the supplementary angle identity

$$\sin A = \sin (180° - A) = - \sin (A - 180°) \qquad (3.4)$$

will determine the setting, and

$$\sin 127° = \sin (180° - 127°) = \sin 53° = 0.798$$

EXAMPLE 3.3F.   Find sin 200°.   *Solution:* From Eq. (3.4)

$$\sin 200° = - \sin (200° - 180°) = - \sin 20° = -0.342$$

EXAMPLE 3.3G.   Find sin 0.7 radians.   It would be possible to graduate the S scale in radians, but it is not common practice on general purpose slide rules.   Radians may be converted to degrees using the relation

$$A° = \frac{180}{\pi} \theta_{rad} \qquad (3.5)$$

$$= 57.3 \theta_{rad}$$

Thus

$$0.7 \text{ rad} = 57.3 \times 0.7 = 40.1°$$

and

$$\sin 40.1° = 0.645$$

Obviously, the inverse trigonometric functions may be as readily found. The two steps in the operating procedure are merely reversed.   Thus, if x_C in Eq. (3.1) is known, to find A:

Set the hairline to x_C on C
Read A beneath the hairline on the appropriate scale, S or ST

EXAMPLE 3.3H.   Find sin⁻¹ 0.755.

Solution: Set 0.755 on C
Read 49° on S

EXAMPLE 3.3I.   Find sin⁻¹ 0.09.

Solution: Set 0.09 on C
Read 5.165° on ST
See Fig. 3.3

The decimal point position, less than 0.1 and greater than 0.01, indicates that the angle is on the ST scale.

EXAMPLE 3.3J.   Find $\sin^{-1} 0.00872$.   This is below the limit of the ST scale, but the angle in radians is very nearly the same numerical value as the sine, or 0.00872, so

$$0.00872 \times 57.3 = 0.50°$$

3.4. Cosines.   The complementary scale relation

$$\cos A = \sin (90° - A) \tag{3.6}$$

forms the basis for reading cosines from the slide rule.   A double valued scale including the complementary angle values is sometimes marked on the S scale.   If this is done, the angle scale for cosines is read in reverse direction without subtracting from 90° to obtain the complement.

The numbers may be placed as in Fig. 3.5, or, on some slide rules, one set of numbers is to the right of the graduation mark and the comple-

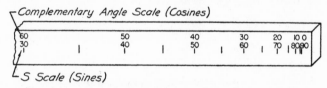

Fig. 3.5.   Complementary Angle Marking for Sine Scale

Operation: Set angle A on S (comp.); read $x = \cos A$ on C

mentary set is to the left of the line.   Sometimes the **complementary** numbers are printed in a different color from the direct set.

EXAMPLE 3.4A.   Find cos 20°.

Solution: Set the hairline to 90° − 20°, or 70° on S (or to 20° on the complementary scale)
  Read 0.94 on C, Fig. 3.3

EXAMPLE 3.4B.   Find cos 85°.

Solution: Set the hairline to 90° − 85°, or 5°, on ST
  Read 0.0872 on the C scale, Fig. 3.3

EXAMPLE 3.4C.   Find cos 89.4°.

Solution: Set the hairline to 90° − 89.4°, or 0.6° on ST
  Read 0.0105 on C
  See Fig. 3.4

EXAMPLE 3.4D.   Find $\cos^{-1} 0.11$.

Solution: Set the hairline to 0.11 on C
  Read 6.32° on S representing 83.68° or read 83.68° on S (comp)
  See Fig. 3.4

3.5. Cosecants and Secants. The trigonometric identities,

$$\csc A = 1/\sin A \tag{3.7}$$

and

$$\sec A = 1/\cos A = 1/\sin (90° - A) \tag{3.8}$$

suggest the way in which these functions can be read directly from the slide rule. Since sine and cosine are read on the C scale, their reciprocals can be found on the C inverted, or CI scale.

EXAMPLE 3.5A. Find csc 7°.

Solution: Set the hairline to 7° on S
Read csc 7° on CI as 8.2

EXAMPLE 3.5B. Find sec 14°.

Solution: Set the hairline to 90° − 14°, or 76°, on S
Read sec 14° on CI scale as 1.03

EXAMPLE 3.5C. Find sec 89°.

Solution: Set the hairline to 1° on ST
Read sec 89° on CI as 57.3

The sines of angles on ST lie between 0.01 and 0.1; their reciprocals lie between 100 and 10, hence 57.3.

EXAMPLE 3.5D. Find $\sec^{-1} 3.15$.

Solution: Set the hairline to 3.15 on CI
1/3.15 appears on C (nearly 0.32)
Read 71.5° on S (complementary scale)

3.6. Problems on Sines and Cosines. Find the sines of the following angles:

	3A	3B	3C	3D	3E
a	30°	70°	2.3°	0°40′	99°
b	62°	7°	0.62°	13°10′	137°
c	17°	1.5°	41.3°	37°50′	171°
d	57°	18.5°	2°20′	0.3 rad	144°
e	39°	0.22°	0.17°	1.1 rad	275°
f	11°	0.45°	0.3°	2.7 rad	307°

Find the smallest positive angle with sine as follows:

				[1]	
g	0.75	0.23	−0.37	0.37	0.122
h	0.92	0.05	−0.88	0.22	0.095

---

[1] Express angles in this column in radians.

	3A	3B	3C	3D	3E
				(1)	
i	0.804	0.082	−0.014	0.85	0.362
j	0.35	0.15	−0.975	0.11	0.177
k	0.165	0.007	−0.037	0.08	0.255
l	0.264	0.003	−0.077	0.81	0.444
m	0.451	0.0061	−0.81	0.97	0.047
n	0.515	0.005	−0.202	0.46	0.015

Find cosines of the following angles:

o	60°	85.5°	77.3°	1.22 rad	−20°
p	69°	86.5°	85.8°	0.087 rad	107°
q	47°	89°	88.2°	1.55 rad	173°
r	76°	5°	61°10′	0.86 rad	285°
s	78°	18°	62°20′	0.13 rad	191°
t	11°	40°	88°20′	1.4 rad	347

Find the smallest positive angle with cosine as follows:

				(1)	
u	0.375	0.0349	−0.423	0.29	0.95
v	0.76	0.057	−0.0262	0.55	0.32
w	0.139	0.191	−0.115	−0.082	0.087
x	0.242	0.0436	−0.749	0.0262	0.0122

3.7. Tangents. It is the practice on almost all slide rules to place the tangent scale on the slide and to associate it with C and CI scales. This is true of all but one of the commercial slide rules shown in the Appendix, Figs. A.1 to A.8. The trigonometric scales in Fig. A.8 are on the frame, and hence the tangent is associated with D, although by aligning the indices, C may be used instead of D.

The sine scale for angles up to 90° often is in two sections, as noted in Art. 3.3 and Fig. 3.3. The tangent scale, however, for first quadrant angles is generally in four sections. The principle underlying each of these sections is discussed separately and then the relationship of the sections is shown. Several examples illustrate the use of the different sections.

The construction equation for the principal section of the tangent scale on the majority of the selected commercial slide rules, ignoring decimal point momentarily, is:

$$\log y_c = \log \tan A_T \ (A_T \text{ from } 5.71° \text{ to } 45°) \qquad (3.2)$$

or

$$y = \tan A$$

---

[1] Express angles in this column in radians.

The operating statement for equating lengths, as indicated by the subscripts, is:

Set the hairline to angle A (5.71° to 45°) on the T scale
Read the tangent, y, on C (0.1 to 1)

The decimal point position is determined by noting that angles from 5.71° to 45° have tangents from 0.1 to 1.

Two alternate scale arrangements are found on commercial slide rules for angles from 45° to 84.29°. One of these, represented by Figs. 3.6 and

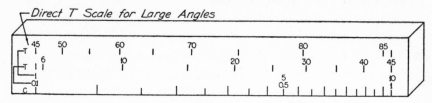

Fig. 3.6. Direct Tangent Scale for Angles Larger than 45°

A.5, includes a T scale in two parts, 5.71° to 45° and 45° to 84.29°, both scale sections being associated with the C scale. The other scale arrangement is based upon the trigonometric identity

$$\tan A = \frac{1}{\tan (90° - A)} = \frac{1}{\cot A} \tag{3.9}$$

If the T scale is marked with complementary angle numbers, Fig. 3.7, as

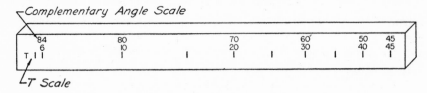

Fig. 3.7. Complementary Angle Marking of Tangent Scale

is the S scale of Fig. 3.5, then from Eq. (3.2) and (3.9)

$$\log y_C = \log \frac{1}{\tan (90° - A_T)}$$

and if

$$A_T' = 90° - A_T$$

$$\log y_C = \log \frac{1}{\tan A_T'}$$
$$= - \log \tan A_T'$$

or

$$- \log y_C = \log \tan A_T' \tag{3.10}$$

Since the CI scale is equivalent to a negative log scale, Eq. (3.10) may be written, ignoring the decimal point,

$$\log y_{CI} = \log \tan A_T \quad (A_T: 45° \text{ to } 84.29°) \qquad (3.11)$$

Thus, for angles greater than 45° and less than 84.29°, the angle value appears on the T scale as the complementary value of the principal angle, and the tangent of the angle is read on the CI scale.   The decimal point range for tangents of angles from 45° to 84.29° is 1 to 10.   The operating statement is:

Set the hairline to A_T (**45° to 84.29°**) on T (Comp)
Read tan A_T on CI (**1 to 10**)

For small angles the tangent is practically equal to the sine.   Therefore, for a third range of angles, 0.57° to 5.71°, the ST scale in association with C may be used for both sine and tangent with an error of less than 0.5 per cent.   The decimal point range, as noted in Art. 3.3, is 0.01 to 0.1.

For large angles, complements of those from 0.57° to 5.71°, the reciprocal form, Eq. (3.9), suggests that the reciprocal C scale, or CI scale could be used.   Therefore:

Set the hairline to complementary values of A (**84.29° to 89.43°**)
on ST
Read tan A on CI (**10 to 100**)

EXAMPLE 3.7A.   Find tan 21°.

Solution: Set the hairline to 21° on T
Read 0.384 on C, Fig. 3.8

EXAMPLE 3.7B.   Find tan 66°.

Solution: Set the hairline to 66° on T (comp)
Read 2.246 on CI, Fig. 3.8

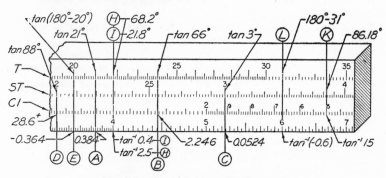

Fig. 3.8.   Scale Settings for Tangents

Examples: 3.7A: tan 21°; 3.7B: tan 66°; 3.7C: tan 3°; 3.7D: tan 88°; 3.7E: tan 160°;
  3.7H: tan⁻¹ 0.4; 3.7I: tan⁻¹ 2.5; 3.7K: tan⁻¹ 15; 3.7L: tan⁻¹ (−0.6)

or on a slide rule with direct T scale associated with C

> Set the hairline to 66° on T (direct)
> Read 2.246 on C

EXAMPLE 3.7C.   Find tan 3°.   *Solution:* The tangent is very closely equal to the sine for small angles (under 6°).   Therefore

> Set the hairline to 3° on ST
> Read 0.0524 on C, Fig. 3.8

EXAMPLE 3.7D.   Find tan 88°.

Solution: Set the hairline to 2° (90°–88°) on ST
> Read 28.6+ on CI, Fig. 3.8

The order of scales on Fig. 3.8 is not exactly like any one of the commercial slide rules shown in the Appendix, but is similar to several of them. In one other respect some of the commercial slide rules differ from Fig. 3.8.   The complementary angle numbers are sometimes printed in red, or sloped, to contrast with the principal values.

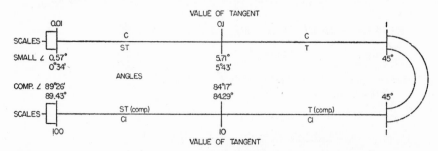

Fig. 3.9.   Diagram of Scales for Reading and Setting Tangents of Angles—Complementary T Scale

Operation: Set angle A on the appropriate scale; read $y = \tan A$ on C or CI as indicated.

Fig. 3.9 shows in diagram form the four sections of tangent scale, and corresponding decimal point position for a slide rule using complementary angle scale with CI for angles between 45° and 89.43°.

Tangents of angles greater than 90° may be found by using trigonometric relationships which reduce them to equivalent first quadrant angles.

EXAMPLE 3.7E.   Find tan 160°.

Solution: The identity

$$\tan A = - \tan (180° - A) = \tan (A - 180°) \qquad (3.11)$$

is useful in this example, and

$$\tan 160° = - \tan (180° - 160°)$$
$$= - \tan 20°$$

Set the hairline to 20° on T
Read 0.364 on C, or tan 160° = −0.364
See Fig. 3.8

EXAMPLE 3.7F.   Find tan 215°.   *Solution:* From Eq. (3.11)

$$\tan 215° = \tan (215° - 180°)$$
$$= \tan 35°$$

Set the hairline to 35° on T
Read 0.70 on C, or tan 215° = 0.70

EXAMPLE 3.7G.   Find tan 0.4°.   *Solution:* This angle is smaller than any readable from the slide rule.   However, the angle in radians is very closely equal to the sine or tangent, and from Eq. (3.3), page 89,

$$\tan 0.4° = 0.01745 \times 0.4 = 0.007$$

If the tangent of an angle is given, the inverse operation can be performed readily.   However, the decimal point position must be carefully watched to determine the scale for setting and reading, Fig. 3.9.

EXAMPLE 3.7H.   Find $\tan^{-1} 0.4$.

Solution: Set hairline to 0.4 on C
Read 21.8° on T
See Fig. 3.8

EXAMPLE 3.7I.   Find $\tan^{-1} 2.5$.

Solution: Set the hairline to 2.5 on CI
Read 68.2° on T (comp)

or, on a slide rule with direct T scale associated with C

Set the hairline to 2.5 on C
Read 68.2° on T (direct)

EXAMPLE 3.7J.   Find $\tan^{-1} 0.03$.   *Solution:* This is in the range of the ST scale.   Therefore

Set the hairline to 0.03 on C
Read 1.72° on ST

EXAMPLE 3.7K.   Find $\tan^{-1} 15.0$.

Solution: Set the hairline to 15 on CI
Read 86.18° on ST (comp)
See Fig. 3.8

EXAMPLE 3.7L.   Find the smallest positive angle for which tan⁻¹ (−0.6).   *Solution:* From Eq. (3.11)

$$\tan^{-1}(-0.6) = 180° - \tan^{-1} 0.6$$

Therefore

Set the hairline to 0.6 on C
Read 31° on T, representing 180° − 31°, or 149°
See Fig. 3.8

3.8. Cotangents.   The reciprocal relationship between tangent and cotangent, Eq. (3.9), makes it possible to modify Fig. 3.9 to indicate settings and readings for cotangents.   The C and CI scales are interchanged, and the limits are reciprocals of the tangent limits, as shown on Fig. 3.10.

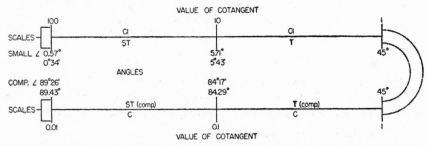

Fig. **3.10.**   Diagram of Scales for Reading and Setting Cotangents of Angles—
Complementary T Scale

Operation: Set angle A on the appropriate scale; read $y = \cot A$ on CI or C as indicated

EXAMPLE 3.8A.   Find cot 40°.

Solution: Set the hairline to 40° on **T**
Read 1.19 on CI

EXAMPLE 3.8B.   Find cot 15°.

Solution: Set the hairline to 15° on **T**
Read 3.73 on CI

EXAMPLE 3.8C.   Find cot 60°.

Solution: Set the hairline to 60° on T (comp)
Read 0.577 on C

or, on a slide rule having direct T scales associated with C for angles above 45°, like Fig. 3.6

Set the hairline to 60° on T (direct)
Read 0.577 on CI

EXAMPLE 3.8D.   Find cot 86°.

Solution: Set the hairline to 4° on ST (90° − 86°)
　　　　　Read 0.0699 on C

If the cotangent of an angle is given, the inverse operation can be performed readily.   However, the decimal point position must be carefully watched to determine the scale for setting and reading.

EXAMPLE 3.8E.   Find cot⁻¹ 1.5.

Solution: Set the hairline to 1.5 on CI
　　　　　Read 33.7° on T

EXAMPLE 3.8F.   Find cot⁻¹ 0.5.

Solution: Set the hairline to 0.5 on C
　　　　　Read 63.4° on T (comp)

or on a slide rule with direct T scale associated with C

　　　　　Set the hairline to 0.5 on CI
　　　　　Read 63.4° on T (direct)

EXAMPLE 3.8G.   Find cot⁻¹ 20.0.

Solution: Set the hairline to 20 on CI
　　　　　Read on ST 2.87°, representing 90° − 2.87°, or 87.13°

3.9. Problems in Tangents and Cotangents.

Find the tangents of the following angles:

	3F	3G	3H	3I	3J
a	14°	50°	69.3°	0.76 rad	−20°
b	25°	75°	89°	0.49 rad	−17°
c	36°	32°	86.42°	0.9 rad	147°
d	42°	55°	66°20′	1.1 rad	127°
e	5.5°	67°	55°10′	0.07 rad	200°
f	3.5°	83°	70°50′	0.04 rad	342°

Find the smallest positive angle with tangent as follows:

				(2)	
g	0.625	0.306	0.82	0.36	2.22
h	0.555	0.94	0.65	1.25	0.17
i	1.28	8.77	−3.08	1.72	0.86
j	0.231	16.4	−0.81	6.68	2.62
k	1.11	28.6	−1.43	−0.38	7.51
l	1.88	0.132	−4.10	−0.70	0.08

───────────

² Express angles in this column in radians.

Find the cotangents of the following angles:

	3F	3G	3H	3I	3J
m	4°20′	8°15′	0.52 rad	88°	62°
n	1°45′	43°	1.2 rad	86°10′	68°30′
o	2.6°	22.4°	0.08 rad	82°15′	56°
p	6.5°	17°	0.73 rad	81°	74°

Find the smallest positive angle with cotangents as follows:

(2)

q	1.27	13.5	0.035	0.21	0.46
r	0.81	17.3	1.92	1.79	0.028
s	0.36	11.2	1.36	0.06	1.30
t	0.19	8.7	0.025	13.0	0.86

3.10. Solution of Oblique Triangles.   A plane triangle contains three sides and three angles; three of these elements must be known, one being a side, if the remaining elements are to be found.   In the study of trigonometry it is evident that the method of solution depends upon the information given.   This is equally true for the slide rule solution of triangles.

If the given information is two angles and a side, or two sides and an angle opposite one of them, the law of sines is well suited for slide rule solution.   Fig. 3.11 and the equation

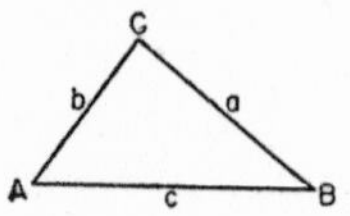

Fig. 3.11.
General Oblique
Triangle Diagram

$$\frac{a}{\sin A} = \frac{b}{\sin B} = \frac{c}{\sin C} = R \qquad (3.12)$$

represent a general triangle.   If at least one numerator quantity in Eq. (3.12) and an associated denominator angle are known, then the ratio, R, is established and three of the remaining triangle elements can be found.   Several examples illustrate the method.

EXAMPLE 3.10A.   Solve the triangle for b, c, C, if $a = 5.0$; $A = 50°$, $B = 60°$.   *Solution:*

$$\frac{5.0_D}{\sin 50°_S} = \frac{b_D}{\sin 60°_S} = \frac{c_D}{\sin C_S} = R$$

Since the sum of angles in a plane triangle is 180°, $A + B + C = 180°$, and $C = 70°$.   The various sines could be read from the slide rule, and C and D scales then used for multiplication or division to find b and c.   But if the sine scale is on the slide and is associated with C, then the continued proportion method of Art. 1.16 and Fig. 1.21, page 35, is easier.   The operating procedure, as denoted by the subscripts in the equation, is

---

² Express angles in this column in radians.

Set the hairline to 5.0 on D
Place 50° on S beneath the hairline
At 60° on S read $b = 5.65$ on D
At 70° on S read $c = 6.13$ on D
See Fig. 3.12

Fig. 3.12. Setting for Oblique Triangle Problem

Example 3.10A: $\dfrac{5}{\sin 50°} = \dfrac{b}{\sin 60°} = \dfrac{c}{\sin 70°}$

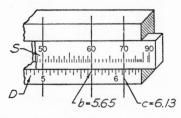

This is equivalent to subtraction of lengths on logarithmic scales, solving

$$\log R_D = \log 5.0_D - \log \sin 50°_S$$
$$= \log b_D - \log \sin 60°_S$$
$$= \log c_D - \log \sin 70°_S$$

If the sine scale is on the frame as in Fig. A.8 in the Appendix, the ratio could be inverted and the C scale used instead of D for the sides.

EXAMPLE 3.10B.   Solve the triangle for b, c, and C if $a = 9.0$; $A = 50°$; $B = 60°$. *Solution:*

$$\frac{9.0_D}{\sin 50°_S} = \frac{b_D}{\sin 60°_S} = \frac{c_D}{\sin 70°_S} = R_D$$

If 50° on S is matched with 9.0 on D, reversal of indices is necessary to read b and c because 60° and 70° on S are beyond the end of D.   If folded scales are available

Set the hairline to 9.0 on DF
Place 50° on S beneath the hairline
At 60° on S read $b = 10.2$ on DF
At 70° on S read $c = 11.05$ on DF

EXAMPLE 3.10C.   Solve the triangle for b, c, and C if $a = 6.7$; $A = 30°$; $B = 40°$. *Solution:*

$$C = 180° - 30° - 40° = 110°,$$

and

$$\frac{6.7}{\sin 30°} = \frac{b}{\sin 40°} = \frac{c}{\sin 110°} = R$$

Again, the use of folded scales permits the solution for b and c without reversal of indices, and since

$$\text{Sin } 110° = \sin (180° - 110°) = \sin 70°$$

Set the hairline to 6.7 on DF
Place 30° on S beneath the hairline
At 40° on S read b = 8.62 on DF
At 70° on S read c = 12.6 on DF

EXAMPLE 3.10D. Solve the triangle for B, C, and c if $a = 8.0$; $A = 50°$; $b = 9.0$. *Solution:*

$$\frac{8.0}{\sin 50°} = \frac{9.0}{\sin B} = \frac{c}{\sin C} = R$$

There are two possible solutions: B may be an acute or an obtuse angle.

Set the hairline to 8.0 on D
Place 50° on S beneath the hairline
At 9.0 on D read on S, B = 59.5°

or choose the supplementary angle, 120.5°, then C may be 70.5° or 9.5°.

At 70.5° on S read 9.84 on D

or

At 9.5° on S read 1.72 on D

EXAMPLE 3.10E. Solve the triangle for B, c, and C if $a = 103$; $A = 80°$; $b = 40$. *Solution:*

$$\frac{103_{DF}}{\sin 80°_S} = \frac{40_{DF}}{\sin B_S} = \frac{c_{DF}}{\sin C_S} = R$$

Folded scales, if available, avoid the necessity for reversing indices, then as denoted by the subscripts

Set the hairline to 103 on DF
Place 80° on S beneath the hairline
At 40 on DF, read B = 22.5° on S
At 180° − 80° − 22.5°, or 77.5°, on S, read 102 on DF

If 80° is the internal angle of the triangle, only one solution for B is possible in this example; the supplementary angle would require that the sum of the angles in the triangle be greater than 180°.

If the given triangle elements are two sides and the included angle, only one answer is possible for the remaining side and angles. However, one of three methods can be used to obtain the solution. The methods are: the law of cosines, the law of tangents, and an altitude-right triangle method. Right triangle methods are discussed in Art. 3.11. The other methods are demonstrated with several examples.

The law of cosines, expressed for finding a, is

$$a = \sqrt{b^2 + c^2 - 2bc \cos A} \qquad (3.13)$$

After a is found, the law of sines may be used for obtaining B and C.

The law of tangents, the alternate method, gives

$$\frac{b+c}{\tan \frac{1}{2}(B+C)} = \frac{b-c}{\tan \frac{1}{2}(B-C)} = S \qquad (3.14)$$

may be solved for $B - C$ since

$$B + C = 180° - A, \text{ or } \frac{1}{2}(B+C) = 90° - \frac{A}{2}$$

The letters representing sides, a, b, c, may be interchanged or rotated in Eq. (3.13) or (3.14) if the corresponding change is made in the angles A, B, C.

EXAMPLE 3.10F. Solve the triangle for a, B, and C if $A = 65°$; $b = 8$; $c = 5$. *Solution:* From the law of cosines

$$a = \sqrt{8^2 + 5^2 - 2 \times 8 \times 5 \cos 65°}$$
$$= \sqrt{89 - 80 \cos 65°} = 7.43$$

The slide rule is hardly needed prior to multiplying 80 by cos 65° which, if the S scale is associated with C, may be done as follows:

Set the right index of C to 80 on D
At 65° on S (comp) read 33.8 on D

Applying the law of sines

$$\frac{7.43_D}{\sin 65°_S} = \frac{8_D}{\sin B_S} = \frac{5_D}{\sin C_S} = R$$

or $B = 77.5°$; $C = 37.5°$
If the law of tangents is used, Eq. (3.14)

$$\frac{8+5}{\tan \frac{115°}{2}} = \frac{8-5}{\tan \frac{1}{2}(B-C)} = S$$

It is possible to solve this equation for $(1/2)(B - C)$ in one slide setting. Sometimes mistakes may be avoided by finding S first, then solving for the angle from

$$\tan\left(\frac{1}{2}\right)(B-C) = \frac{3}{S}$$

Since $B + C = 115°$ and $B - C = 40°$, one may check the values of B and C by using the law of sines.

EXAMPLE 3.10G. Solve the triangle for a, B, and C if $A = 100°$; $b = 9$; $c = 7$. *Solution:* From the law of cosines

$$a = \sqrt{9^2 + 7^2 - 2 \times 9 \times 7 \cos 100°}$$
$$= \sqrt{130 - 126 \cos 100°}$$

Since cos 100° is negative

$$a = \sqrt{130 - (-21.9)} = 12.32$$

and

$$\frac{12.32}{\sin 100°} = \frac{9}{\sin B} = \frac{7}{\sin C}$$

From the law of tangents

$$\frac{9 + 7}{\tan 40°} = \frac{9 - 7}{\tan (1/2)(B - C)} = S$$

$S = 19.1$ and $(1/2)(B - C) = 6°$, or $B - C = 12°$, then $B = 46°$; $C = 34°$

EXAMPLE 3.10H. Solve the triangle for a, B, and C if $A = 30°$, $b = 8$; $c = 2$. *Solution:* From the law of cosines

$$a = \sqrt{68 - 32 \cos 30°} = 6.36$$

and

$$\frac{6.36}{\sin 30°} = \frac{8}{\sin B} = \frac{2}{\sin C}$$

Angle B, being opposite the longest side must be the largest angle, and if the angles are to add to 180°, must be obtuse; or $B = 141°$; $C = 9°$

Applying the law of tangents

$$\frac{10}{\tan 75°} = \frac{6}{\tan (1/2)(B - C)} = 2.68$$

from which $B - C = 132°$, and again $B = 141°$; $C = 9°$.

If the given data are three sides, the solution for angles is quite laborious, whether slide rule or other methods are used. An application of the law of cosines represents one method of solution. The formula for tangent of a half angle is another method:

$$\tan \frac{1}{2} A = \frac{r}{s - a} \tag{3.15}$$

where

$$s = \left(\frac{1}{2}\right)(a + b + c) \tag{3.16}$$

$$r = \sqrt{\frac{(s - a)(s - b)(s - c)}{s}} \tag{3.17}$$

EXAMPLE 3.10I. Solve the triangle for A, B, and C if $a = 7$; $b = 8$; $c = 9$. *Solution:* From Eq. (3.17)

$$s = \frac{7 + 8 + 9}{2} = 12$$

And Eq. (3.18)

$$r = \sqrt{\frac{(12-7)(12-8)(12-9)}{12}} = \sqrt{5} = 2.236$$

and

$$\tan\left(\frac{1}{2}\right) A = \frac{2.236}{5} = 0.4472$$

or

$$A = 48.2°$$

In a similar manner $B = 58.4°$; $C = 73.4°$. If the law of cosines is used

$$\cos C = \frac{49 + 64 - 81}{2 \times 7 \times 8} = \frac{32}{112} = \frac{2}{7} = 0.286$$

and

$$C = 73.4°$$

3.11. Solution of Right Triangles. In the applications of the slide rule, to engineering particularly, right triangle problems arise much more frequently than oblique triangles. Also, as mentioned in Art. 3.10, some oblique triangle problems can be solved conveniently by erecting an altitude and solving as two right triangles.

The same general methods of attack are appropriate for right triangles as for oblique triangles, but with one angle equal to 90° the calculations are usually simplified. Referring to Fig. 3.13, and the law of sines, Eq. (3.12)

$$\frac{a}{\sin A} = \frac{b}{\sin B} = \frac{c}{\sin 90°} = \frac{c}{1} \qquad (3.18)$$

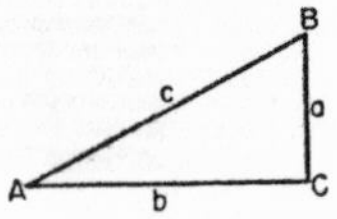

Fig. 3.13. General Right Triangle Diagram

This can be used to solve all problems for which the given data are sides or angles of the right triangle, although if the legs, a and b, are the given data, the tangent or cotangent relationship, or the Pythagorean theorem must be used first. If side a and angle B are known, A can be found from the complementary angle relationship

$$A = 90° - B \qquad (3.19)$$

If the sine scale of the slide rule carries complementary angle marking, as shown in Fig. 3.5, mental subtraction is not necessary; a setting can be made on the complementary angle scale as a graphical means of subtraction.

The following examples illustrate the procedure for several typical problems.

EXAMPLE 3.11A. Solve the right triangle if $a = 6$; $A = 40°$. *Solution:*

$$\frac{6_D}{\sin 40°_S} = \frac{b_D}{\sin 50°_S} = \frac{c_D}{1}$$

Using the continued proportion method of Fig. 1.21, page 35, and assuming that the S scale is associated with the C scale, the procedure is

Set the hairline to 6 on D
Place 40° on S beneath the hairline
At 50° on S read $b = 7.15$ on D
At 90° (the right index) on S read $c = 9.34$ on D
See Fig. 3.14

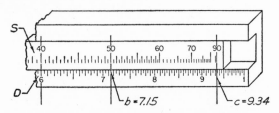

Fig. 3.14. **Setting for Right Triangle Problem**

Example 3.11A: $\dfrac{6}{\sin 40°} = \dfrac{b}{\sin 50°} = c$

EXAMPLE 3.11B. Solve the right triangle if $a = 9$; $A = 40°$. *Solution:*

$$\frac{9_{DF}}{\sin 40°_S} = \frac{b_{DF}}{\sin 50°_S} = c_{DF}$$

if a is set on the D scale for this example, 50° on S is off scale, making it necessary to reverse indices to read b. If folded scales are available, the problem can be solved in one slide setting as follows:

Set the hairline to 9 on DF
Place 40° on S beneath the hairline
At 50° on S read $b = 10.73$ on DF
At 90° on S read $c = 14.0$ on DF

The use of folded scales will not avoid reversing indices for all problems. Example 3.11C is one.

EXAMPLE 3.11C. Solve the right triangle if $a = 3$; $A = 15°$. *Solution:*

$$\frac{3}{\sin 15°} = \frac{b}{\sin 75°} = c$$

Set the hairline to 3 on D
Place 15° on S beneath the hairline
At the left index of S read c = 11.6 on D
Hold this position with the hairline and move slide to place right
    index of S at the hairline (11.6)
At 75° on S read b = 11.2

EXAMPLE 3.11D.   Solve the right triangle if $a = 4$; $B = 32°$. *Solution:*

$$\frac{4}{\sin A} = \frac{b}{\sin 32°} = c$$

If the S scale is marked with complementary angle values, subtraction
of 32° from 90° is not necessary.   The operation may be

Set the hairline to 4 on D
Place 32° on S (comp) beneath the hairline
At 32° on S(direct) read b = 2.50 on D
At 90° on S read c = 4.72 on D

EXAMPLE 3.11E.   Solve the right triangle if $c = 8$; $a = 4.5$.   With
the hypotenuse, c, known, the slide rule operation is essentially the same
as above, but the sequence of setting is changed slightly.   *Solution:*

$$\frac{8}{\sin 90°} = \frac{4.5}{\sin A} = \frac{b}{\sin B}$$

Set 90° on S to 8 on D
At 4.5 on D read A = 34.2°
By subtracting from 90° or reading on the S(comp) scale B = 55.8°
At 55.8° on S read b = 6.62 on D

EXAMPLE 3.11F.   Solve the right triangle if $c = 4$; $A = 43.2°$.
Solution:

$$4_D = \frac{a_D}{\sin 43.2°_S} = \frac{b_D}{\sin B_S}$$

Set 90° on S to 4 on D
At 43.2° on S read a = 2.74 on D
By subtracting from 90° or reading on S(comp) B = 46.8°
At 46.8° on S read b = 2.92 on D

EXAMPLE 3.11G.   Solve the right triangle if $A = 3°$; $c = 6000$.
Solution:

$$6000 = \frac{a}{\sin 3°} = \frac{b}{\sin 87°}$$

Set the index of S to 6000 on D
At 3° on ST read a = 314 on D

Since $\sin 87°$ is hardly readable on the S scale, b cannot be found with accuracy from this equation. The approximation method of Example 2.10L, page 81, gives much greater accuracy, and

$$b = 6000 - \frac{314^2}{12,000} = 5991.8$$

EXAMPLE 3.11H. Solve the right triangle if $a = 9$; $b = 5$. The angles opposite the given sides are not known, so the law of sines cannot be used directly. Since $a/b = \tan A$, this offers a method for finding angles A and B. In a form ready for setting on the slide rule

$$\frac{5_D}{\tan A_T} = \frac{9_D}{1_C}$$

Set the hairline to 5 on D
Place the index of C (45° on T) to 9 on D
Read on T scale $A = 29°$; $B = 61°$
Move the slide to place 29° on S beneath the hairline
Read on D opposite the left index $c = 10.3$

The latter two steps solve

$$\frac{5}{\sin 29°} = \frac{c}{1}$$

EXAMPLE 3.11I. Solve the right triangle if $a = 7$, $b = 80$. Again, one solution is:

$$\frac{7}{\tan A} = 80$$

Angle A is too small to appear on the T scale, so it may be read very closely using ST. Or,

$$c = 80 + \frac{7^2}{2 \times 80} = 80.306$$

and

$$80.306 = \frac{7}{\sin A}$$

from which, on ST, angle A is found to be 5.00°; then $B = 85.00°$.

EXAMPLE 3.11J. Solve the triangle of Fig. 3.15 using right triangles.

Fig. 3.15. Triangle Problem: Given Two Sides and Included Angle

Example 3.11J: $\dfrac{h}{\sin 27°} = 22 = \dfrac{r}{\sin 63°}$

Solution:

$$\frac{h}{\sin 27°} = \frac{22}{1} = \frac{r}{\sin 63°}$$

The setting is not described, but the results are $h = 10.0; r = 19.6$; then $s = 10.4$. With h and r known, $B = 43.8°$ can be found as in the preceding examples. The side, p, may be found from

$$p = \sqrt{h^2 + s^2}$$
$$= \sqrt{10.0^2 + 10.4^2} = 14.43$$

The law of sines provides a check on these results and

$$\frac{22}{\sin 43.8°} = \frac{14.43}{\sin 27°} = \frac{30}{\sin 109.2°}$$

Sometimes a trigonometric function of the angle is known instead of the angle. The function may not be the one most convenient for solution of the triangle. This introduces one more step into the problem, and requires either finding the angle from the function or using a different method of solution.

EXAMPLE 3.11K. Solve the right triangle if $\cos A = 0.45; c = 5.0$.
Solution:

$$\frac{b}{c} = 0.45 = \frac{b}{5.0}$$

or this may be written in the law of sines form

$$\frac{b_\mathrm{D}}{0.45_\mathrm{C}} = \frac{5_\mathrm{D}}{1_\mathrm{C}} = \frac{a_\mathrm{D}}{\sin A_\mathrm{S}}$$

Set the right index of the C scale to 5.0 on D
At 0.45 on C read $b = 2.25$ on D
Also at 0.45 on C read $B = 26.8°$ on S
At 26.8° on S (comp) read $a = 4.46$

One setting of the slide is required for this example.

EXAMPLE 3.11L. Solve the right triangle if $\sin A = 0.3; b = 6$.
Solution: Mistakes are less likely if one first finds $A = 17.5°$ and proceeds as in Examples 3.11B or 3.11D. $a = 1.89; c = 6.29$.

EXAMPLE 3.11M. Solve the right triangle if $\tan A = 0.6; a = 3$.
Solution: From the T and C scales angle A may be found to be 31°, then proceed as in Example 3.11A. $b = 4.99; c = 5.82$.

EXAMPLE 3.11N. Solve the right triangle if $\tan A = 1.8; c = 1.5$.
Solution: From the CI and T(comp) scales angle A may be found to be 61°, then proceed as in Example 3.11F. $a = 17.4; b = 5.37$.

$$\frac{15_\mathrm{D}}{1_\mathrm{C}} = \frac{A_\mathrm{D}}{\sin 61°_\mathrm{S}} = \frac{b_\mathrm{D}}{\sin (90° - 61°)_{\mathrm{S\,comp}}}$$

3.12. Trigonometric Equations. If a series of values of angle A are given and the values of x for

$$x = k \sin A \qquad (k = \text{constant})$$

are wanted, it is not necessary to read sin A from the scale and then set it on D or C to perform the multiplication by k. If the sine scale is associated with C, a setting to angle A, on S or ST is equivalent to setting sin A on the C scale. Therefore

> Set the index of C to k on D
> Move the hairline to successive values of A on S or ST
> Read values of x on D

The decimal point position of sin A must be watched, 0.01 to 0.1 on ST; 0.1 to 1 on S. If A has a single value instead of a series, one setting only of the hairline on the sine scale is required.

EXAMPLE 3.12A.   Calculate $x = 7.5 \sin A$ for $A = 5°$, $10°$, $15°$, $20°$.

Solution: Set the index of C to 7.5 on D

> At $5°$ on ST, $10°$, $15°$, and $20°$ on S read 0.653, 1.30, 1.94, and 2.56 on D

A series of multiplications by cos A can be carried out the same way if the angle setting is on the complementary numbers of S or ST.

EXAMPLE 3.12B.   Calculate $x = 1.10 \cos A$ for $A = 10°$, $20°$, $30°$. *Solution:* If folded scales are used, all values can be obtained with one slide setting.

> Set the index on C to 1.10 on DF
> At $10°$, $20°$, and $30°$ on S(comp) read 1.083, 1.035, and 0.953 on DF

The slide rule of Fig. A.2, page 183, has an S scale associated with B. Therefore, the foregoing examples could be solved on this slide rule using A and B scales for multiplication, with settings to the angles on S.

If the equation to be solved for several angle values is

$$x = k \tan A \qquad (k = \text{constant})$$

the same general method of operation is used except that successive settings are on the tangent in place of the sine scale. However, this is satisfactory only for portions of the range of angle A which are in association with the C scale. If A exceeds $45°$, for example, and tan A would be read on CI, the multiplication procedure must be changed. As shown in Chapter 1, multiplication using D and CI (for tan A) is:

> Set the hairline to k on D
> Place angle A, if tan A appears on CI, on T (comp.) beneath the
>   hairline
> Read the product, x, on D opposite the index

EXAMPLE 3.12C.   Calculate $x = 3.9 \tan A$ for $A = 5°$, $20°$, $40°$, $60°$. *Solution:* The tangents of three of these angles appear on C, but if $60°$ is on T (comp), a separate setting is necessary for that one.

Set the right index of C to 3.9 on D
At 5° on ST read $x = 0.340$ on D
At 20° on T read $x = 1.42$
At 40° on T read $x = 3.28$
Set the hairline to 3.9 on D
Place 60° on T (comp) beneath the hairline
Read $x = 6.75$ on D at the index

If a direct T scale in association with C is available, the latter three steps for 60° are not necessary.

Obviously, multiplication of k by any other of the trigonometric functions can be performed in a manner like either the 3.9 tan 60° or 3.9 tan 40° depending upon whether the function would be read on the CI or C scales.

The foregoing examples solve for x when k and angle A are given. If x and k are the given quantities in

$$\frac{x}{k} = \sin A \, ; \frac{x}{k} = \cos A \, ; \frac{x}{k} = \tan A$$

the scales and the setting are the same, but the sequence of operations is changed to

At successive values of x
Read angle A on the appropriate trigonometric scale

EXAMPLE 3.12D.   Calculate $y = \sin^2 A$ for $A = 10°, \ 20°, \ 30°$.
Solution:

Set the hairline successively to 10°, 20°, 30°, on S
Read on B 0.0302, 0.117, and 0.25

The relationship of C scale to B (Chapter 2) permits direct reading of $\sin^2 A$ in this way.   It would be necessary to read the values of $\sin A$ and re-set to obtain $\sin^2 A$ if a slide rule not equipped with A or B scales is used.

3.13. Summary, Chapter 3.   The theoretical principle of the trigonometric scales as well as practical matters of scale graduation, range of application, and operating procedures are summarized, thus providing a short review to the reader who has discontinued for a time the use of the trigonometric scales of the slide rule.   Also included is a review of the slide rule solution of triangles.   Article numbers and Figure numbers in parentheses refer to more complete explanations and to examples.

1. *Principle of Trigonometric Scales.*   (Art. 3.1)   The basic trigonometric scales on the slide rule usually are the sine and tangent placed in association with one of the log scales (often C) so that, by equating

lengths,

$$\log x_C = \log \sin A_8 \tag{3.1}$$
$$\log x_C = \log \tan A_T \tag{3.2}$$

from which

$$x_C = \sin A_8$$
$$x_C = \tan A_T$$

The solution of triangles requires division or multiplication of trigonometric functions by lengths of sides; or, by subtracting or adding lengths on log scales

$$\log A_D \pm \log \sin A_8 = \log R_D$$

or

$$\log A_D \pm \log \tan A_T = \log Q_D$$

In other words any one of the equations

$$\frac{a}{\sin A} = R; \text{ or, } a \sin A = R$$

and

$$\frac{a}{\tan A} = Q; \text{ or } a \tan A = Q$$

may be directly solved on the slide rule. The subscripts denote scale names on which reading or setting is commonly made.

2. *Recognition of Trigonometric Scales.* (Art. 3.1) A sine scale on a strange slide rule often can be recognized and the method of operation learned by examining it for a pair of scales on which 30° matches 0.5, 90° matches 1.0, and 1° matches sin 1° or 0.01745. Likewise, the tangent scale and its method of operation may be determined from the fact that tan 26.5° is slightly less than 0.5 and tan 45° is 1.0.

3. *Scale Graduations.* (Art. 3.2, Figs. 3.1, 3.2) On 10-inch slide rules the finest subdivision intervals usually are:

	Basic Angle Range	
Tangent Scale	Sine Scale	Finest Subdivision
	0.57°–5.74°	0.02°
5.71°–10°	5.75°–10°	0.05°
10°–30°	10°–20°	0.1°
30°–45°	20°–30°	0.2°
	30°–60°	0.5°
	60°–80°	1°
	80°–90°	5°

Scales subdivided in minutes are graduated the same as above for angles greater than 30° on the the sine scale.   For the remainder of the range, the interval is 10', 5', 2' or 1' (Fig. 3.2).

4. *Operation Procedure for Trigonometric Functions.*   (Arts. 3.3, 3.4, 3.5, 3.7, 3.8; Figs. 3.3–3.10)   The usual procedure for reading sin A or tan A in the basic range is

Set the hairline to angle, A, on S, ST, or T
Read sin A or tan A on C

Outside of the basic range, several trigonometric relations are useful

$$\sin (180° - A) = \sin A \qquad (3.4)$$

$$\tan (90° - A) = \frac{1}{\tan A} \qquad (3.9)$$

$$\tan (180° - A) = \tan A \qquad (3.11)$$

Cosines may be read using sine scale and either graphic complementary angle scale or arithmetic subtraction, since

$$\cos A = \sin (90° - A) \qquad (3.6)$$

The functions of cosecant, secant, and cotangent are reciprocals of sine, cosine, and tangent, respectively, and hence are readable on CI scale if the latter appear on C.

$$\csc A = \frac{1}{\sin A} \qquad (3.7)$$

$$\sec A = \frac{1}{\cos A} \qquad (3.8)$$

$$\cot A = \frac{1}{\tan A} \qquad (3.9)$$

5. *Range of Scales.*   (Figs. 3.5, 3.9, 3.10)   Decimal point position on trigonometric scales must be used as marked.   The usual ranges of values readable from the slide rule are: 0.01 to 1 for sine and 0.01 to 100 for tangent, with other functions corresponding.   In graphic form for many commercial slide rules

Scale		C		C		
Sine		0.01		0.1		1
Angle		0.57°		5.74°		90°
Scale			ST		S	

Scale		C		C	CI(or C³)		CI	
Tangent	0.01		0.1		1		10	100
Angle	0.57°		5.71°		45°		84.29°	89.43°
Scale		Use ST		T	T(comp) or T³		ST (comp)	

[3] Fig. 3.6.   Direct T scale.

6. *Solution of Triangles.* (Art. 3.10, 3.11) The continued proportion form of the law of sines is convenient for slide rule calculations in solving many triangle problems, both oblique and right angle. (Fig. 3.11)

$$\frac{a}{\sin A} = \frac{b}{\sin B} = \frac{c}{\sin C} = R \tag{3.12}$$

If given a right triangle (Fig. 3.13) with $C = 90°$, then Eq. (3.12) is simplified because $\sin C = 1$, and $R = c$. Eq. (3.18)

If the given data are such that R is known or can be found from a given a and A, or b and $\sin B$, or c and C, then a single setting of the slide and movement of the hairline only will obtain the other elements. In particular, if the sine scales are on the slide and associated with C scale

> **Set the hairline on D (or DF) to a, or b, or c, whichever is known**
> **Place the slide with angle A, or B, or C on S or ST matching the corresponding a, or b, or c**
> **Move the hairline to other known numerator terms on D (or DF) or denominator terms on the slide**
> **Read answers on the matching scale**

If $\sin B$ is known rather than angle B, set $\sin B$ on the C scale, and read B on S or ST in passing.

Independently of the slide rule, it may be necessary to find one angle from

$$A + B + C = 180°$$

or if $C = 90°$

$$A + B = 90°$$

Not all triangle problems can be solved by law of sines. (Examples 3.10 F, G, H.) The more laborious law of cosines

$$a = \sqrt{b^2 + c^2 - 2bc \cos A} \tag{3.13}$$

or law of tangents

$$\frac{b + c}{\tan (1/2)(B + C)} = \frac{b - c}{\tan (1/2)(B - C)} \tag{3.14}$$

may be required. If three sides are given (Example 3.10I), solution may be obtained by the half angle formula.

In right triangle problems and in other calculations (Art. 3.11), tangent and cosine definitions

$$\frac{a}{\tan A} = b; \frac{b}{\tan B} = a; \frac{b}{\cos A} = c; \frac{a}{\cos B} = c$$

may be solved for one of the terms by the same procedure as outlined for law of sines.

7. *Trigonometric Equations.* (Art. **3.12**) It would be possible, by equating lengths on the appropriate scales, to read log sin A, log cos A, log sec A, and so on, from a slide rule. However, these quantities are very seldom useful in slide rule calculations. More often, $\sin^2 A$, $\cos^2 A$, $\tan^2 A$, are useful quantities. Obviously, they can be obtained by reading sin A, cos A, or tan A and then squaring the result.

If the S scale is associated with C and the slide rule has an A or B scale, $\sin^2 A$ may be read directly.

> Set angle A on S
> Read $\sin^2 A$ on B

The K, $\sqrt{}$ or R, and $\sqrt[3]{}$ scales make possible direct reading of cubes, square roots, or cube roots of trigonometric functions appearing on C. (See Chapter 2.)

Also, it should be apparent that if $1/\sin^2 A$, $1/\tan^2 A$, or $1/\sqrt{\cos A}$ is wanted, the slide can be withdrawn and inserted inverted as a means of direct reading on A scale, or $\sqrt{}$ scale, for a series of values of angle.

3.14. Problems on Chapter 3. Solve the following, using a slide rule.

	3K	3L	3M	3N
a	sec 4.5°	sec 12°10′	csc 3.5°	csc 9°10′
b	sec 18°	sec 14°15′	csc 27.5°	csc 1°20′
c	sec 80°	sec 88°40′	csc 75°	csc 21°40′
d	sec 1.5°	sec 42°	csc 42°	csc 62°30′
e	sec⁻¹ 13.5	sec⁻¹ 47.5	csc⁻¹ 1.96	csc⁻¹ 15.5
f	sec⁻¹ 2.6	sec⁻¹ 8.2	csc⁻¹ 17.5	csc⁻¹ 3.8
g	sec⁻¹ 9.4	sec⁻¹ 1.15	csc⁻¹ 37.5	csc⁻¹ 4.2
h	sec⁻¹ 1.3	sec⁻¹ 3.9	csc⁻¹ 8.5	csc⁻¹ 86

Refer to the right triangle diagram, Fig. 3.13, and solve for the missing sides and angles.

i	a:22; A:17°	a:52; b:85	c:170; A:25°	b:11; A:8°
j	a:0.46; B:26°	a:13; C:18°	c:35; B:19°	b:32; B:19°
k	a:0.88; b:0.32	a:75; A:29°	a:1.75; b:4.9	c:2.62; B:47°
l	b:1.23; c:6.24	a:162; B:36°	a:79; c:95	a:0.06; b:0.09
m	a:56.2; A:86°	b:93; c:530	a:8.4; A:62°	a:0.37; c:5.2
n	c:12.6; B:2.5°	b:0.81; A:7°	a:140; B:56°	a:12; A:17°
o	b:6.75; B:41°	b:2.6; B:2.5°	b:13; c:65	a:820; B:82°
p	c:146; A:21°	c:42; B:13°	b:375; c:580	b:9.1; c:11

Refer to the general triangle diagram, Fig. 3.11, and solve for the missing sides and angles.

3P	3Q
a $a:13; b:17; B:40°$	$a:12.7; b:39; C:95°$
b $a:9; A:16°; B:75°$	$a:914; B:16°; C:49°$
c $b:2.5; B:62°; C:18°$	$b:65; A:9.5°; C:120°$
d $b:125; c:47; B:32°$	$a:370; b:40; C:71°$
e $a:52; c:95; A:4°$	$b:21; c:18; A:45°$
f $b:76; c:82; B:65°$	$b:460; A:29°; C:62°$
g $a:42; A:15°; C:45°$	$b:59; A:35°; B:97°$
h $b:11; c:7.5; C:17°$	$c:162; A:16°; B:61°$
i $a:80; b:90; \cos A:0.65$	$a:16; b:45; \tan B:0.75$
j $b:15; c:42; \tan C:1.10$	$b:19; c:16; \cos B:0.18$
k $a:42; \cos B:0.52; C:90°$	$a:4.8; c:75; \cos B:0.05$
l $c:19; \tan B:0.37; \sin C:0.85$	$a:6.2; \tan A:0.07; C:90°$

Solve the following with minimum possible slide movement:

	3R	3S	3T
a	$\sin^2 16°$	$\cos^2 47°$	$\tan^2 25°$
b	$\sin^2 70°$	$\cos^2 62°$	$\tan^2 67°$
c	$1/\sin^2 9°$	$1/\cos^2 41°$	$1/\tan^2 18°$
d	$1/\sin^2 55°$	$1/\cos^2 82°$	$1/\tan^2 50°$
e	$\sqrt{\sin 77°}$	$\sqrt{\cos 19°}$	$\sqrt{\tan 40°}$
f	$\sqrt{\sin 4°}$	$\sqrt{\cos 15°}$	$\sqrt{\tan 77°}$
g	$\sin^3 19.5°$	$\cos^3 50°$	$\tan^3 61°$
h	$\sin^3 63°$	$\cos^3 21°$	$\tan^3 4°$

If angle A is 5°, 20°, 40°, 60°, 75°, 85°, calculate the following:

i	$8.7 \sin A$	$14.2 \cos A$	$\dfrac{\pi}{18} \tan A$
j	$38 \sin A$	$0.92 \cos A$	$47 \tan A$
k	$19.6/\sin A$	$48/\cos A$	$136/\tan A$
l	$390/\sin A$	$1.3/\cos A$	$62/\tan A$

Calculate the following for values of A from 0° to 360° in 30° steps and plot on polar coordinate paper:

m	$R = 7 \sin \dfrac{A}{2}$	$R = 3.5 \sin \dfrac{A}{4}$	$R = 3.5 \cos^2 A$
n	$R = 3.5 \sin \dfrac{A}{2}$	$R = 7 \sin^2 A$	$R = 3.5 \sin \dfrac{A}{4}$
o	$R = 7 \sin \dfrac{A}{3}$	$R = 3.5 \sin^2 A$	$R = 0.1\theta^2$ (radians)
p	$R = 7 \sin \dfrac{A}{4}$	$R = 7 \cos^2 A$	$R = 0.5\theta$ (radians)

LOGARITHMIC AND EXPONENTIAL
CALCULATIONS

4.1. Exponents and Logarithms Principles. Several properties of exponents are fundamental to the mathematical operations of this chapter. One may refer to a book on algebra for proof of these relationships. The correctness of the formulas may be verified by substituting simple numbers such as 2, 3, 4, 5, or 6 for the various letter symbols in Eqs. (4.1) to (4.6).

$$a^x a^y = a^{x+y} \tag{4.1}$$

$$\frac{a^y}{a^x} = a^{y-x}; \text{ if } y = 0, \frac{1}{a^x} = a^{-x} \tag{4.2}$$

$$(a^x)^y = a^{xy} \tag{4.3}$$

$$\sqrt[x]{a^y} = a^{y/x}; \text{ if } y = 1, \sqrt[x]{a} = a^{1/x} \tag{4.4}$$

Certain factoring operations, Eq. (4.5) and (4.6), in which exponents arise also are useful in some problems.

If
$$c = a \times b$$

then

$$c^x = (ab)^x = a^x b^x; \sqrt[x]{c} = \sqrt[x]{ab} = \sqrt[x]{a} \times \sqrt[x]{b} \tag{4.5}$$

If
$$d = \frac{a}{b}$$

then

$$d^x = \left(\frac{a}{b}\right)^x = \frac{a^x}{b^x}; \quad \sqrt[x]{d} = \sqrt[x]{\frac{a}{b}} = \frac{\sqrt[x]{a}}{\sqrt[x]{b}} \tag{4.6}$$

The exponents, x and y, may be positive or negative, whole numbers, fractions, or decimal numbers.

A general definition of a logarithm and some of its properties also is important to this chapter. If

$$M = b^x$$

and

$$N = b^y$$

then by definition of a logarithm

$$x = \log_b M \tag{4.7}$$
$$y = \log_b N \tag{4.8}$$

where b is called the base of logarithms. In principle b may be any number, but in practice two values only are used, 10 and e, where e is $2.71828 \cdots$. Logarithms to the base 10 are called common logarithms, and to the base e are called natural logarithms.

From Eq. (4.1), if

$$P = M \times N = b^x \times b^y = b^{x+y}$$
$$\log_b P = \log_b (M \times N) = x + y \tag{4.9}$$

and if

$$Q = \frac{N}{M} = \frac{b^y}{b^x} = b^{y-x}$$

or

$$\log_b Q = \log_b \left(\frac{N}{M}\right) = y - x \tag{4.10}$$

Also, from Eq. (4.3) if

$$R = M^k = b^{kx} \tag{4.11}$$

then

$$\log_b R = \log_b M^k = kx = k \log_b M \tag{4.12}$$

where k may be positive, negative, whole number, fraction, or decimal number.

Chapter 1 is concerned with the solution of Eqs. (4.9) and (4.10) by addition and subtraction on log scales with base, b, equal to 10. Extension to more than two quantities also is a part of Chapter 1. A major part of Chapter 2 is devoted to the solution of Eq. (4.11) or (4.12) by equating slide rule lengths for k equal to 1/3, 1/2, 2, or 3. This chapter deals with the use of the slide rule in the solution of these equations for k having any value.

From the form of Eq. (4.11) it may appear that R is the quantity sought.   This is not always the case.   One may wish to determine k, or M, or x, all of the terms but one being known.

If a table of logarithms is available, as it is in graphic form on nearly all commercial slide rules, Eq. (4.12) can be solved by using the full-length log scales of the slide rule for any multiplications or divisions by k, Art. 4.4.   Or, if Eq. (4.12) is written

$$\log (\log_b R) = \log k + \log (\log_b M) \tag{4.13}$$

it is in a form for solution with the LogLog slide rule, Arts. 4.8 and 4.9.

The sequence and content of topics throughout the book have been determined partly in a manner which places the most widely useful material first, and also introduces the simple scale arrangement or method before discussing the more complex.   Consequently, the use of the L scale is presented in the next several articles preceding the discussion of LogLog scales and their uses.

4.2. The Log Scale and Logarithms of Numbers. A uniformly graduated scale, usually marked L, and sometimes placed on the slide, can be used along with C or D scales to find logarithms to base 10. Among the eight commercial slide rules shown in the Appendix, Figs. A.1 to A.8, an L scale is on the frame of five, and on the slide of three (Figs. A.1, A.5, and A.6).

The introduction to log scales in Chapter 1, Fig. 1.4, shows the principle and relationship of the L scale to C and D scales.   In equation form

$$L_L = \log M_D \tag{4.14}$$

represents by the subscripts the scales on which the logarithm, L, or anti-logarithm, M, are found.

In general only the mantissa of the logarithm is read from the L scale, but Fig. 4.1 shows that it would be possible to obtain the logarithmic characteristic if the D scale were extended.

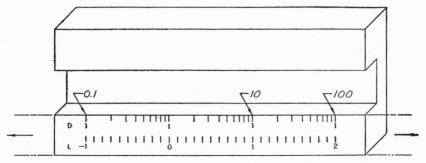

Fig. 4.1.   Model of Slide Rule for Reading Logarithm Complete with Characteristic

A portion of the L scale and D scale, fully graduated, are shown in Fig. 4.2 and several examples are illustrated thereon. The finest L scale graduation interval on 10-inch slide rules generally is 0.002.

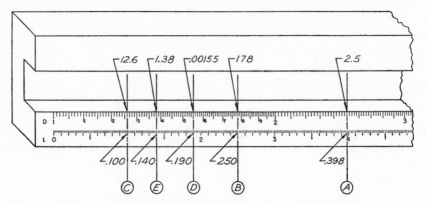

Fig. 4.2. Scale Settings for Logarithms and Antilogarithms

Examples: 4.2A:log 2.50; 4.2B:log 178; 4.2C:log 12.6; 4.2D:log 0.00155; 4.2E:antilog 0.140

EXAMPLE 4.2A.   Find log 2.50.

Solution: Set the hairline to 2.50 on D
        Read 0.398 on L
        See Fig. 4.2

EXAMPLE 4.2B.   Find log 178.

Solution: Set the hairline to 178 on D
        Read the mantissa, 0.250, on L

The logarithmic characteristic, equal to the correction number as used in Chapter 1, is 2; therefore, log 178 = 2.250.   See Fig. 4.2.
EXAMPLE 4.2C.   Find log 12.6.

Solution: Set the hairline to 12.6 on D
        Read the mantissa, 0.100, on L

The characteristic is 1; therefore, log 12.6 = 1.100.   See Fig. 4.2.
EXAMPLE 4.2D.   Find log 0.00155.

Solution: Set the hairline to 0.00155 on D
        Read the mantissa, 0.190, on L
        See Fig. 4.2

The characteristic is −3, and the answer may be written several different ways:

$\overline{3}.190$ meaning $-3 + 0.190$
$7.190 - 10$
-2.810

For subsequent slide rule calculations the last form is usually preferable. Except for the 2, it can be read directly from the slide rule.

Set 0.00155 on CI
Read -0.810 on L

EXAMPLE 4.2E.   Find antilog 0.140.

Solution: Set the hairline to 0.140 on L
Read 1.38 on D
See Fig. 4.2

Since the characteristic is zero, the decimal point follows the first digit.
EXAMPLE 4.2F.   Find antilog 1.740.

Solution: Set the hairline to the mantissa, 0.740, on L
Read 5.50 on D

The characteristic is 1, and the decimal point position, therefore, is 55.0.
EXAMPLE 4.2G.   Find antilog 8.920 − 10.

Solution: Set the hairline to 0.920 on L
Read 8.32 on D

The characteristic is −2; the answer is 0.0832.
EXAMPLE 4.2H.   Find antilog −1.650.

Solution: Set the hairline to 0.650 on L
Read 2.24 on CI, aligned with D

Since the given number is equivalent to 8.350 − 10, the characteristic is −2, and the decimal point position is at 0.0224.
EXAMPLE 4.2I.   Find antilog $\overline{3}.69$.

Solution: Set the hairline to 0.69 on L
Read 4.90 on D

or since the characteristic is −3, the answer is 0.00490.
EXAMPLE 4.2J.   Find ln[1] 2.86.
The general relationship between logarithms to the base e and logarithms to the base 10 for any number, S, is:

---

[1] This is a common method for writing logs to the base e to distinguish them from logs to the base 10, occurring in the preceding examples.

$$\log_e S = \frac{\log_{10} S}{\log_{10} e} \tag{4.15}$$

or since $\log_{10} e = 0.4343 \cdots$

$$\ln S = \frac{1}{0.4343} \log S = 2.303 \log S \tag{4.16}$$

For the particular example, using D and L scales

$$\log 2.86 = 0.455$$

and using C and D scales for multiplication

$$\ln 2.86 = 2.303 \times 0.455 = 1.05$$

EXAMPLE 4.2K.   Find ln 38.0.

Solution: Set the hairline to 38.0 on D
       Read the mantissa, 0.58, on L

or

$$\log 38.0 = 1.58$$

and using C and D scales

$$\ln 38.0 = 2.303 \times 1.58 = 3.64$$

EXAMPLE 4.2L.   Find ln 0.036.

Solution: Set the hairline to 0.036 on CI aligned with D
       Read -0.443 on L

or

$$\ln 0.036 = -1.443 \times 2.303 = -3.32$$

EXAMPLE 4.2M.   Find antiln 13.7.

Solution: If $13.7 = \ln S$, then $\log S = 13.7/2.303 = 5.95$
       Set the hairline to 0.95 on L
       $+5$
       Read 8.92 on D

or

$$\text{Antiln } 13.7 = 8.92 \times 10^5$$

EXAMPLE 4.2N.   Find antiln -2.60.

Solution: Antiln $-2.60 =$ antilog $(-2.60/2.303)$
                     $=$ antilog (-1.13)
       Set the hairline to 0.13 on L
       Read on CI aligned with D, 7.42

or since $-1.13 = 8.87 - 10$

$$\text{Antiln } -2.60 = 0.0742$$

4.3. Problems in Logarithms.

	4A	4B	4C	4D

Find logarithms to the base 10 for the following numbers.

	4A	4B	4C	4D
a	2.20	0.640	2710	0.0092
b	7.35	0.076	750	0.215
c	188	0.0292	35	0.041
d	845	0.091	8800	0.003

Find antilogarithms (base 10) for the following

	4A	4B	4C	4D
e	0.260	9.17 − 10	3.053	$\bar{2}.42$
f	0.736	−1.28	1.44	$\bar{1}.037$
g	1.938	−0.36	2.76	$\bar{3}.56$
h	2.82	7.25 − 10	4.33	0.295

Find logarithms to the base e for the following numbers.

	4A	4B	4C	4D
i	1.40	0.082	5300	0.364
j	3.70	0.0065	1540	0.111
k	560	0.93	628	0.007
l	82	0.014	17.28	0.66

Find antilogarithms (base e) for the following

	4A	4B	4C	4D
m	3.20	−1.62	1.065	12.75
n	0.82	−2.56	7.41	−3.06
o	0.174	−0.821	9.86	−0.040
p	1.86	−7.30	0.93	−0.195

4.4. Powers and Roots of Numbers.   If Eq. (4.12) is written

$$(\log R)_{\mathrm{D}} = k_{\mathrm{C}}(\log M)_{\mathrm{D}}$$

the subscripts denote the scales on which reading or setting of the quantities may be made in raising M to any power, k.   The quantity, $\log M$, may be found on the L scale, or at least the mantissa for it is read from L.   Similarly, if R is being sought, its mantissa is set on L.

If k or M is the unknown, an inverse operation is required, but the same scales are used for the several terms.

Slide rule methods for solving typical problems in powers and roots are illustrated by several examples.   The examples have been chosen to show positive and negative exponents, and numbers smaller than 1 as well as numbers larger than 1.

EXAMPLE 4.4A.   Find $R = 2.5^{1.7}$.   *Solution:* From the fundamental property of logarithms, Art. 4.1, it is evident that

$$\log R = 1.7 \log 2.5$$

and from Example 4.2A, log 2.5 = 0.398.   Using C and D scales for the multiplication

$$\log R = 1.7 \times 0.398 = 0.677$$

To find R = antilog 0.677

Set the hairline to 0.677 on L
Read R = 4.75 on D

EXAMPLE 4.4B.   Find $R = 178^{0.72}$.   *Solution:* log R = 0.72(log 178). From Example 4.2B, log 178 = 2.250, and using C and D scales for multiplication

$$\log R = 0.72 \times 2.250 = 1.62$$

To find R = antilog 1.62

Set the hairline to the mantissa, 0.62, on L
Read 4.17 on D, representing 41.7

EXAMPLE 4.4C.   Find $R = 1/12.6^{1.4}$.   *Solution:* Since $1/12.6^{1.4} = 12.6^{-1.4}$

$$\log R = -1.4(\log 12.6)$$
$$= -1.4 \times 1.100 = -1.54$$

Antilog (-1.54) may be found by using the inverted scale.

Set the hairline to 0.54 on L
Read 2.88 on CI

Like Example 4.2G, the logarithmic characteristic is -2, and the decimal point position, $R = 0.0288$.

EXAMPLE 4.4D.   Find $R = \sqrt[2.2]{800}$.   *Solution:* From Eq. (4.4)

$$\log R = \frac{1}{2.2} \log 800 = \frac{1}{2.2} 2.903 = 1.320$$

and

$$\text{antilog } 1.32 = 20.9$$

EXAMPLE 4.4E.   Find $R = 0.00155^{1.6}$.   *Solution:*

$$\log R = 1.6(\log 0.00155)$$

and from Example 4.2D, log 0.00155 is 7.19 − 10, or $\overline{3}.19$, or −2.81. Multiplication is easier if the latter form is used and

$$\log R = 1.6(-2.81) = -4.50, \text{ or } 5.50 - 10$$
$$-5$$
$$\text{antilog } (5.50 - 10) = 3.16$$

If the multiplication is carried to one more decimal place of accuracy by the methods of Art. 1.15, the answer is $3.\overset{-5}{1}75$.

EXAMPLE 4.4F. Find $R = 0.080^{-1.2}$. *Solution:*

$$\log R = -1.2(\log 0.080)$$

However, since log 0.080 is negative, log R is a positive quantity. Fewer mistakes are likely to result if it is written

$$R = 0.080^{-1.2} = \left(\frac{1}{0.08}\right)^{1.2} = 12.5^{1.2}$$

then

$$\log R = 1.2(\log 12.5)$$
$$= 1.2 \times 1.096 = 1.315$$

from which

$$R = 20.65$$

EXAMPLE 4.4G. Find k if $7^k = 25$. *Solution:*

$$k \log 7 = \log 25$$

or

$$k = \frac{\log 25}{\log 7} = \frac{1.398}{0.847} = 1.65$$

EXAMPLE 4.4H. Find k if $320^k = 0.0026$. *Solution:*

$$k \log 320 = \log 0.0026$$

or

$$k = \frac{\log 0.0026}{\log 320} = \frac{7.415 - 10}{2.505} = \frac{-2.585}{2.505}$$
$$= -1.032$$

EXAMPLE 4.4I. Find $R = \dfrac{280^{5.2}}{5000^{5.2}}$. *Solution:* The calculation for this example may be shortened if, in accordance with Eq. (4.6), it is written

$$R = \left(\frac{280}{5000}\right)^{5.2} = 0.056^{5.2}$$

then

$$\log R = 5.2(\log 0.056)$$
$$= 5.2(0.748 - 2) = 5.2(-1.252)$$
$$= -6.51 = 3.49 - 10$$

and

$$R = 3.09 \times 10^{-7}$$

EXAMPLE 4.4J. Find $R = 17^{0.4} \times 6^{1.3}$. *Solution:* For a product of quantities, the logs are added, Eq. (4.1)

$$\begin{aligned} \log R &= 0.4(\log 17) + 1.3(\log 6) \\ &= 0.4 \times 1.23 + 1.3 \times 0.778 \\ &= 0.492 + 1.011 = 1.503 \end{aligned}$$

then

$$R = 31.8$$

EXAMPLE 4.4K. Find $R = \dfrac{75^{4.2}}{15^{2.16}}$. *Solution:* The log of the denominator term is subtracted, Eq. (4.2), and

$$\begin{aligned} \log R &= 4.2(\log 75) - 2.16(\log 15) \\ &= 4.2 \times 1.875 - 2.16 \times 1.176 \\ &= 7.875 - 2.540 = 5.335 \end{aligned}$$

from which

$$R = 2.16 \times 10^{5}$$

4.5. Problems in Powers and Roots. Calculate the following:

	4E	4F	4G	4H
a	$3^{2.5}$	$0.7^{2.6}$	$\sqrt[2.2]{15}$	17^{-3}
b	4.5^{6}	$0.865^{0.7}$	$\sqrt[1.4]{76}$	$700^{-0.2}$
c	$500^{0.6}$	0.49^{10}	$\sqrt[3.6]{527}$	$625^{-0.11}$
d	$45^{2.5}$	$0.28^{1.4}$	$\sqrt[0.8]{2.6}$	$22^{-0.46}$
e	$1.5^{2.7}$	$0.982^{4.21}$	$\sqrt[1.2]{1.65}$	$2400^{-0.016}$
f	1.22^{7}	$0.77^{3.9}$	$\sqrt[7.5]{92}$	$0.96^{-5.2}$
g	$1.025^{6.5}$	$0.31^{4.52}$	$\sqrt[3.2]{1.111}$	$0.17^{-0.052}$
h	$22^{0.032}$	$0.87^{11.5}$	$\sqrt[7.5]{5000}$	$0.076^{-0.3}$
i	$1600^{0.0022}$	$0.006^{0.015}$	$\sqrt[365]{202}$	$1.19^{-3.6}$
j	$87^{0.115}$	$0.121^{0.07}$	$\sqrt[46]{36}$	$1.52^{-0.22}$
k	$1700^{1.35}$	$0.91^{0.37}$	$\sqrt[2.2]{37,000}$	$5800^{-1.2}$
l	$1.006^{0.037}$	$0.0015^{0.02}$	$\sqrt[77]{1.52}$	$1,800,000^{-0.035}$
m	$4.7^{2.4}$	$3.95^{3.1}$	$15.2^{-1.2}$	$900^{-2.3}$
n	$3.5^{1.8}$	$13.2^{1.82}$	$750^{-2.8}$	$5.88^{-6.7}$
o	$1.75^{0.36}$	$4.25^{0.16}$	$1.27^{-0.035}$	$4.82^{-0.31}$
p	$12^{0.67}$	$7.3^{0.44}$	$2.13^{-0.73}$	$7.35^{-0.28}$

4.6. Principle and Arrangement of LogLog Scales. Distances along the C and D scales are proportional to the logarithms of the numbers marked on the scale. In like manner, distances along the LogLog scales are proportional to logarithms of the logarithms of the numbers marked on the LL scales. The LogLog scales could have any number as base, but since only 10 and e are customary bases, one or both of these are used in practice. The particular commercial slide rules in the Appendix, Figs. A.3 to A.8, have been selected partly because they represent several different ways of making and marking LogLog scales.

The form of construction equation for a number of these commercial slide rules, Figs. A.3, A.4, A.6, A.7, A.8, is a mixture of base 10 and base e

$$L_\mathrm{L} = \log \ln M_\mathrm{LL}$$

and for Fig. A.5 it is base 10 throughout

$$L_\mathrm{L} = \log \log M_\mathrm{LL}$$

The subscripts, as elsewhere in the book, represent scales for setting or reading.
Consequently

Set the hairline to M on LogLog scale
Read on L scale $L = \log \ln M$, or $L = \log \log M$ (except for
log characteristic)

The value of loglog M or log ln M is very seldom of any practical use. If, instead of reading on L, lengths are equated on D and the LogLog scales the equation solved is

$$\log y_\mathrm{D} = \log \ln M_\mathrm{LL}$$

or

$$y_\mathrm{D} = \ln M_\mathrm{LL} \tag{4.17}$$

and

$$\log y_\mathrm{D} = \log \log M_\mathrm{LL}$$

or

$$y_\mathrm{D} = \log M_\mathrm{LL} \tag{4.18}$$

The operating statements are

Set the hairline to the number, M, on LL
Read $y_D = \ln M_\mathrm{LL}$ on D (Figs. A.3, A.4, A.6, A.7, A.8)
Read $y_D = \log M_\mathrm{LL}$ on D (Fig. A.5)

Figs. 4.3, 4.4, and 4.5 show for the several commercial slide rules the LogLog scale points of fold and scale designation as well as decimal point position and relationship to the full-length log scales.

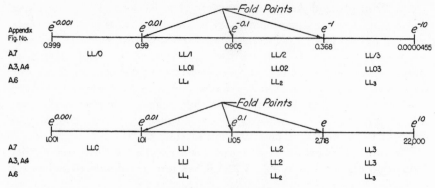

Fig. 4.3　Diagram of Scale Designations and Fold Points for LogLog Scales on Selected Commercial Slide Rules

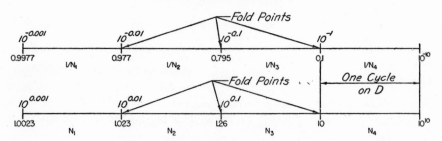

Fig. 4.4.　Diagram Showing Fold Points for LogLog Scales on Deci-LogLog Slide rule, Fig. A.5

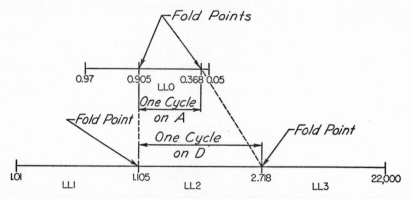

Fig. 4.5.　Diagram Showing Fold Points and Scale Associations for LogLog Scales on LogLog Trig Slide Rule, Fig. A.8

The LogLog scales are placed on the frame and are generally associated with the D scale, but the slide rule of Fig. A.8 has a portion of its LogLog scale associated with the A scale, Fig. 4.5.

The finest LogLog graduation interval, as on the other slide rule scales, is 1, 2, or 5 times 0.01, 0.001, 0.0001 for the small number range, or times

10, 100, and so forth on the large number portion of the scale. Through-out most of its range the LogLog scale is more "non-uniform" than the log or trig scales, and consequently the subdivision interval changes many times.

An interesting property of the LogLog scales shown diagrammatically in Figs. 4.4 and 4.6 is that reciprocals complete with decimal point can be read; for example, by setting on LL3 and reading on LL03.

4.7. Logarithms of Numbers by LogLog Scales. The L along with C and D scales enable one to find logs of any number to base 10 or e, as shown in Art. 4.2. The LogLog scale is no better for the purpose except in the range of numbers from about 0.4 to 2.5, in which interval greater accuracy of reading is possible. This greater accuracy of reading is par-ticularly evident near 1. Above 4 and below 0.25 the LogLog scale is noticeably less accurate. The theoretical points of equal accuracy by both methods are at e, (2.718), and $1/e$, (0.368).

Like the trigonometric scales, these scales must be read as marked; shifting the decimal point in numbers on the LogLog scales is incorrect. The range of numbers on the commercial LogLog scales is satisfactory for most practical applications, but special methods may be needed to obtain an answer for very large or very small numbers, or to attain desired accuracy.

As shown by Eqs. (4.17) and (4.18), page 127, some commercial LogLog scales are constructed to read logarithms to base 10 in association with the D scale, whereas others give logarithms to base e in association with the D scale. The constant ratio between logs to the two bases, Eq. (4.16), makes it possible to shift the slide by the constant ratio and read to another base on the C or CF scale as shown by some of the later examples, 4.7K and 4.7L.

Settings for several examples are tabulated for convenience in com-paring them.

Example	Problem	Scales Set on	Read on	Answer
4.7A	ln 15,000	LL3, LL$_3$ N$_4$	D DF/$_M$	9.62
4.7B	ln 1.152	LL2, LL$_2$ N$_2$	D DF/$_M$	0.1415
4.7C	ln 1.0375	LL1, LL$_1$ N$_2$	D DF/$_M$	0.0368
4.7D	ln 1.003	LL0 (Versalog) N$_1$	D DF/$_M$	0.00300

These examples are on various sections of the LL scales, and the decimal point positions of the answers also differ according to the LL scale on which setting is made, Fig. 4.4. For Example 4.7D, 1.003 is below the scale limit of several of the commercial slide rules, but for numbers near 1, a very close approximation is:

$$\ln V = V - 1 \qquad (V\text{: } 0.99 \text{ to } 1.01) \tag{4.19}$$

At the extreme limits, 0.99 and 1.01, the error is one-half of 1 per cent; nearer 1 it is much less.

The LogLog scales of the Model 2 slide rule, Fig. A.5, having scales marked N_4, $1/N_4$, etc., are based upon

$$\log_{10} \log_{10} M_{\text{LL}}$$

Therefore, to find $\ln M$, it is necessary to multiply $\log M$ by 2.303, Eq. (4.16). The scales $DF/_M$ and $CF/_M$ are folded at 2.303, and setting on any one of the scales N_4, N_3, N_2, N_1, and reading on $DF/_M$ accomplishes this multiplication without the use of the slide. The range of numbers and logarithms is:

Set on N_4; Read $\ln M$ on $DF/_M$, 2.3 to 23
Set on N_3; Read $\ln M$ on $DF/_M$, 0.23 to 2.3
Set on N_2; Read $\ln M$ on $DF/_M$, 0.023 to 0.23
Set on N_1; Read $\ln M$ on $DF/_M$, 0.0023 to 0.023

EXAMPLE 4.7E.   Find $\ln 60{,}000$ using LogLog scales.

Solution: This number is out of range on some of the commercial slide rules, but

$$4 \times 15{,}000 = 60{,}000$$

and

$$\ln 4 + \ln 15{,}000 = \ln 60{,}000$$

or

$$\ln 60{,}000 = 1.385 + 9.62 = 11.105$$

It can be read directly without factoring from $DF/_M$ scale

Set hairline to 60,000 on N_4
Read 11.10 on $DF/_M$

In the equations defining a logarithm

$$M = b^x; \quad x = \log_b M \tag{4.7}$$

M can be less than 1 only if x is negative. In other words, the logarithms of numbers less than 1 are negative regardless of the base. Several examples of logarithms for numbers less than 1 and the commercial slide rule settings are:

Example	Problem	Scales		Answer
		Set on	Read on	
4.7F	ln 0.9846	LL01	D	−0.015
		LL/1	D	
		$1/N_1$	DF/M	
4.7G	ln 0.866	LL02	D	−0.144
		LL/2	D	
		LL0 (Fig. A.8)	A	
		$1/N_2$	DF/M	
4.7H	ln 0.262	LL03	D	−1.34
		LL/3	D	
		LL0 (Fig. A.8)	A	
4.7I	ln 0.998	LL0 (Fig. A.7)	D	−0.002

As for Example 4.7D, a slide rule is not needed to obtain ln 0.998; see Eq. (4.19).

EXAMPLE 4.7J.   Find ln 10^{-7}.   *Solution:* This can be read from DF/M if set on $1/N_4$.   Or, because log $10^{-7} = -7$, the 2.303 relationship between logs to base 10 and base e enables one to calculate it.

$$\ln 10^{-7} = 2.303(-7) = -16.12$$

Logarithms to base 10 can be read as readily as logarithms to base e using LogLog scales.

EXAMPLE 4.7K.   Find log 250 using LogLog scales.

Solution: Set the hairline to 10 on LL3 or LL_3
        Place 1 on CF beneath the hairline
        At 250 on LL3 read 2.40 on CF

Using D and L scales and determining the characteristic independent of the slide rule, one more decimal place is obtainable, or 2.398.   If the CF scale is used as described rather than C, a wider range of numbers and their logs is readable without moving the slide.

EXAMPLE 4.7L.   Find log 1.0182 using LogLog scales.

Solution: With the same slide setting as for Example 4.7K

    At 1.0182 on LL1 or LL_1 read 0.00783 on CF

Using D and L scales, Art. 4.2, one digit only is readable, 0.008.

Examples of antilogarithms using LogLog scales are not included; the reader may profitably use the examples and problems of Art. 4.3 for practice.

4.8. Powers and Roots of Numbers Using LogLog Scales.   The two-variable mathematical relationships solved by slide rule require equating lengths.   Relationships involving three variables require addition or subtraction of lengths on the appropriate scales.   And the three-variable equation

$$R = M^k \tag{4.11}$$

in the form

$$\log (\log_b R) = \log (\log_b M) + \log k \tag{4.13}$$
$$\text{LL} \qquad\qquad \text{LL} \qquad\quad \text{C}$$

indicates the addition, and by the letters below the equation, shows the scales of the slide rule commonly used for the operation. Fig. 4.6 shows

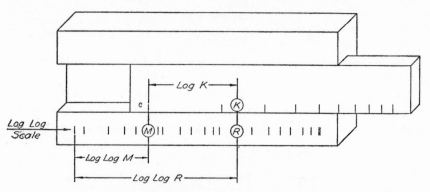

Fig. 4.6. Principle of LogLog Scales for Powers of Numbers

LogLog R = Log K + LogLog M; or
Log R = K (Log M)

or

$$R = M^k$$

the method of operation graphically. The particular sections of the LogLog scales depend upon the numerical values involved. Also, if log k is negative, the operation becomes a subtraction.

As a further general observation about Eq. (4.13) and its solution, it makes no difference whether base, b, is 10 or$_1$ e. For Fig. A.5 it is 10; for the other selected commercial slide rules it is e.

The operating statement is:

> **Set the hairline to M on the LogLog scale**
> **Place the index of C beneath the hairline**
> **At k on C read $R = M^k$ on LL**

The CI scale may be used in place of C if the operation is correspondingly modified, just as is the case in division or multiplication

> **Set the hairline to M on the LogLog scale**
> **Place k on CI beneath the hairline**
> **At the index of CI read $R = M^k$ on LL**

This method has the same advantage as multiplication using CI and D; no decision is necessary regarding right or left index on the slide; use whichever one is within the frame.   However, for introductory purposes adding a length, log k, using the C scales seems less likely to lead to error; the examples, therefore, describe C scale use.   The decimal point position and the sign of k determine whether the answer is read on the same section or a different section of the LogLog scales.   Several examples illustrate these matters.

EXAMPLE 4.8A.   Calculate $3^{1.2}$ using LogLog scales.

Solution: Set the hairline to 3 on LL3, LL$_3$, or N$_3$
Place the index of C beneath the hairline
At 1.2 on C read 3.74 on the same section of LL scales
See Fig. 4.7

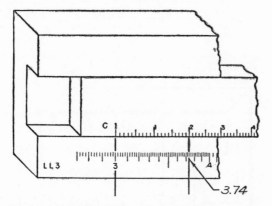

Fig. 4.7.   Scale Setting for Number Raised to Power
Example 4.8A: $3^{1.2} = 3.74$

EXAMPLE 4.8B.   Calculate $3^{0.12}$.

Solution: Set the hairline to 3 on LL3, LL$_3$, or N$_3$
Place the index of C beneath the hairline
At 0.12 on C read 1.141 on LL2, LL$_2$ or N$_2$

For $k = 0.12$, log k is negative, one full log cycle less than log 1.2, hence the answer is read on the next lower section of the LogLog scales, Figs. 4.3 and 4.4.

EXAMPLE 4.8C.   Calculate $3^{0.012}$.

Solution: Set the hairline to 3 on LL3, LL$_3$, or N$_3$
Place the index of C beneath the hairline
At 0.012 on C read 1.0133 on LL1, LL$_1$, or N$_1$

In this example log k is 2 cycles less than log 1.2.   If the problem were $3^{0.0012}$ the answer would be very close to 1, and less than 1.01.   This is below the range of LogLog scale on most of the commercial slide rules, but usually either 1 or 1.01 is accurate enough.

EXAMPLE 4.8D.   Calculate 3^{12} using LogLog scales.

Solution: Set the hairline to 3 on N_3
    Place the index of C beneath the hairline
    At 12 on C read 5.3×10^5 on N_4

The answer to this problem is beyond the range of LL3 and LL_3 scales. However, if factored into $3^6 \times 3^6$, one can read $3^6 = 730$ from LL3, and square it by one of the methods described in Chapter 2.

EXAMPLE 4.8E.   Calculate $0.9^{1.32}$.

Solution: Set the hairline to 0.9 on LL02, LL/2, LL_2, $1/N_2$
    Place the index of C beneath the hairline
    At 1.32 on C read 0.87 on the same section of LL scales
    See Fig. 4.8

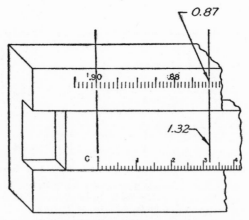

Fig. 4.8.   **Scale Setting for Number Less than 1 Raised to Power**
Example 4.8E: $0.90^{1.32} = 0.87$

Using a slide rule such as Fig. A.8 on which LogLog scales for numbers less than 1 are in association with B, the above operation is correct if C scale is replaced by B scale.

EXAMPLE 4.8F.   Calculate $0.9^{0.132}$.   *Solution:* The decimal point shift from 1.32 in Example 4.8E to 0.132 indicates that the exponent is one full cycle below 1.32 on C, or the answer is read on LL01, LL/1, LL_1, or $1/N_1$ for the several commercial slide rules, or is 0.9862.

EXAMPLE 4.8G.   Calculate $0.9^{13.2}$.   *Solution:* The answer is one cycle of C in the opposite direction from Example 4.8F, or is 0.249 read on LL03, LL/3, LL_3, or $1/N_3$.

EXAMPLE 4.8H.   Calculate 5^{-3} using LogLog scales.

Solution: Set the hairline to 5 on LL3, etc.
Place the index of C beneath the hairline
At 3 on C read 5^3 on LL3 (as 125)

or

$1/5^3$ appears on LL03 as 0.008

Similarly, a number on LL01, LL02, or LL03 raised to a negative power will have the answer on the reciprocal scale: LL1, LL2, LL3. This way for raising numbers to negative powers is impossible on a slide rule such as Fig. A.8, on which the numbers greater than 1 on the LogLog scales are associated with D, and numbers less than 1 are associated with A scale. Reciprocals or negative powers must be found as a separate operation with such a slide rule.

EXAMPLE 4.8I. Calculate 0.4^{-2}.

Solution: Set the hairline to 0.4 on LL02, LL/2, LL_2 or $1/N_3$
Place the index of C beneath the hairline
At 2 on C, 0.4^2 appears on LL03, etc.

and

$0.4^{-2} = 6.25$ on the LL3, or equivalent numbers-greater-than-one scale

EXAMPLE 4.8J. Calculate $R = \sqrt[2.25]{17}$. *Solution:* Several ways for writing this example are

$$R = 17^{1/2.25}$$

$$\log R = \frac{1}{2.25}\log 17$$

$$\operatorname{loglog} R = \operatorname{loglog} 17 + \log 1 - \log 2.25$$
$$\text{LL} \qquad\qquad \text{LL} \qquad\qquad\qquad \text{C}$$

or

Set the hairline to 17 on LL3
Place 2.25 on C beneath the hairline
Read 3.52 on LL3

The ratio, $1/2.25 = 0.445$, could be determined using CI and C scales, thus reducing this example to the form of a power like the others in this article.

4.9 Exponential Equations. Products or sums of logarithmic or exponential quantities can be calculated easily if taken one step at a time.

EXAMPLE 4.9A. Calculate $7.3 \ln \dfrac{82}{45} - 2.4 \ln \dfrac{4.7}{52}$

Solution: Calculate 82/45, and 4.7/52
Find ln 1.825, and ln 0.0904
Multiply by 7.3 and 2.4 respectively
Subtract the two terms

EXAMPLE 4.9B. Calculate $y = 18^{0.05t}$ for a series of values of t. *Solution:* Mistakes are less likely if a tabular method is used for problems like this. However, it is possible to make one, or perhaps two, slide settings for the entire series within the range of the LogLog scales.

t	$0.05t$	$y = 18^{0.05t}$
5	0.25	2.06
10	0.5	4.25
15	0.75	8.75
20	1	18
25	1.25	37
30	1.5	76

When $t = 20$, $0.05t = 1.0$, and $18^{1.0} = 18$
The one-setting procedure is evident as:

Set the hairline to 18 on LL3, etc.
Place $t = 20$ on C beneath the hairline
At successive values of t on C read the other amounts

EXAMPLE 4.9C. Calculate $y = \dfrac{15}{4.1} e^{-1.75} {}^{-0.5t}$ for a series of values of t. *Solution:* This is shortened by reducing $0.5/1.75$ to 0.276. It is possible in this example also to find $e^{-0.276t}$ in one slide setting for a series of values of t. These then may be multiplied by $15/4.1$ in another slide setting. The method is left for the reader to devise. As check points, for $t = 5$ and $t = 10$, $e^{-0.276t} = 0.306$ and 0.093.

EXAMPLE 4.9D. Calculate $y = e^{-0.5t} \sin 2\pi t$ for a series of values of t. *Solution:* A tabular method, and the use of trigonometric scales are indicated. The suggested column headings only are given.

t	$0.5t$	$e^{0.5t}$	$2\pi t$	Angle $2\pi t$ in degrees	$\sin 2\pi t$	y

4.10. Summary, Chapter 4. 1. *Graphic Table of Functions.* The slide rule, in many respects, is a graphical table of mathematical functions which offers speed and convenience in calculation at some sacrifice in accuracy. However, the accuracy attainable is well within practical limits for a great many computation purposes, and the visual interpolation along slide rule scales is easier than numerical interpolation in a table.

In addition to being a handy table of functions, the slide rule readily performs operations on some of the tabular data, as in solving a triangle by the law of sines, for example.

The LogLog scales provide even more ease in computation, particularly in raising numbers to powers that are not simple integers or fractions as they are in Chapter 2. But any problem which can be solved on

LogLog scales also can be solved on a slide rule not so equipped, but it may require a few more operations.

The particular tables of functions which are the subject of this chapter are

$$M = 10^x; \text{ or } x = \log M \qquad \text{(Arts. 4.2, 4.7, Fig. 4.2)}$$
$$M = e^x; \text{ or } x = \ln M \qquad \text{(Arts. 4.2, 4.7)}$$
$$R = M^k; \text{ or } k = \log_M R \qquad \text{(Art. 4.8, Figs. 4.7, 4.8)}$$
$$L = \log \ln M \qquad \text{(Art. 4.6)}$$
$$L = \text{loglog } M \qquad \text{(Art. 4.6)}$$

2. *Principle of Scales.* The uniform L scale in association with D solves by equating lengths

$$M = 10^x; \text{ or } x = \log M$$

The LogLog scales in association with a log scale, D, DF/$_M$, or C solves

$$M = e^x; x = \ln M$$

or

$$M = 10^x; x = \log M$$

as well as

$$R = M^k; k = \log_M R$$

3. *Recognition of Scales.* A uniform scale is easily recognized on a strange slide rule. To be useful for logs, 0.301 on the uniform scale should match 2 on a log scale, and 0.602 should match 4.

LogLog scales can be recognized and the scales they are associated with can be determined from the fact that 10 to 100 on LL equals the distance from 1 to 2 on the associated log scale; and from 0.2 to 0.02 equals the distance from 1 to 2 on its associated log scale.

4. *Operating Procedures.* The equation

$$L_\text{L} = \log M_\text{D} \qquad (4.14)$$

indicates by subscripts the usual scales for reading and setting to solve for M or L. Powers of numbers such as

$$R = M^k \qquad (4.11)$$

can be found by reading log M on L and using C and D scales to multiply by k. The inverse operation determines R.

The LogLog scale settings on commercial slide rules for natural logs are indicated by subscripts

$$x_\text{D} = \ln M_\text{LL}$$

or on Fig. A.5

$$x_{\text{DF/M}} = \ln M_{\text{LL}}$$

Using LogLog scales

$$R = M^k \tag{4.11}$$

is solved by adding lengths on scales denoted by subscripts in the form

$$\underset{\text{LL}}{\text{loglog } R} = \underset{\text{LL}}{\text{loglog } M} + \underset{\text{C}}{\log k} \tag{4.13}$$

Any log scale on the slide may be used in place of C. In particular, subtracting a negative length on CI is often more convenient, but perhaps more likely to be incorrectly done by the unpracticed.

Sometimes R or M are larger or smaller than the scale range permits. Factoring in one of the following ways aids in calculating such problems.

$$R = (M^{k/2})^2 = (M^{k/3})^3 = M(M^{k-1}) = M^2(M^{k-2})$$

or

$$R = (M^{2k})^{1/2} = (M^{3k})^{1/3} = a^k \left(\frac{M}{a}\right)^k$$

4.11. Problems on Chapter 4. The group of problems in Art. 4.5 also is suitable for solution using LogLog scales.

4I	4J	4K	4L

Solve each of the following problems using the CI scale for the exponent; check some with the C scale.

	4I	4J	4K	4L
a	$22^{0.36}$	$150^{0.24}$	$0.7^{0.41}$	$0.95^{0.21}$
b	$1100^{-0.13}$	$4000^{0.08}$	$1.039^{0.015}$	$0.12^{0.042}$
c	$550^{-0.15}$	$0.07^{-0.03}$	$0.97^{6.2}$	$0.8^{3.5}$
d	$1350^{1.03}$	$1.32^{3.8}$	$850^{-0.23}$	$0.19^{-0.08}$

All of the problems in each of the following rows can be solved in one slide setting by a suitable choice of slide scale (C, CI, CIF, or CF) for the exponent.

	4I	4J	4K	4L
e	$50^{1.2}$	$50^{1.7}$	$50^{0.92}$	$50^{-0.8}$
f	$4^{4.5}$	$4^{0.45}$	$4^{0.045}$	$4^{-0.45}$
g	$0.8^{1/3.6}$	$0.8^{-0.53}$	$0.8^{2.6}$	$0.8^{-0.15}$
h	$0.3^{1.6}$	$0.3^{0.16}$	$0.3^{1/3.1}$	$0.3^{-0.41}$

4I	**4J**	**4K**	**4L**

Calculate the following:

i $17 \times 8^{-0.65}$ $\qquad$ $0.023 \times 16^{3.5}$ $\qquad$ $47 \times 5.7^{-0.37}$ $\qquad$ $480 \times 0.6^{0.3}$

j 14^{70} $\qquad$ $17^{7.2}$ $\qquad$ $0.975^{1.7}$ $\qquad$ $0.036^{-0.07}$

k $e^{6.8}$ $\qquad$ $(e^{1.8} - e^{-1.8})/2$ $\qquad$ $0.52 \times 8^{-0.4}$ $\qquad$ $e^{1/2.4}$

l $(e^{0.56} + e^{-0.56})/2$ $\qquad$ $e^{-0.037}$ $\qquad$ 1.032^{125} $\qquad$ $e^{-1/0.83}$

4M

Calculate and plot each of the following on semi-log paper.

a $y = 1.5 \times 10^{0.06t}$ $\qquad$ $t(0 \text{ to } 10)$

b $y = 2.1 \times 10^{0.03t}$ $\qquad$ $t(0 \text{ to } 20)$

c $y = 3.6 \times 10^{0.23t}$ $\qquad$ $t(0 \text{ to } 2)$

d $y = 4.2 \times 10^{-0.26t}$ $\qquad$ $t(0 \text{ to } 2)$

e $y = 4.8 \times 10^{-0.042t}$ $\qquad$ $t(0 \text{ to } 10)$

f $y = 6.3 \times 10^{-0.036t}$ $\qquad$ $t(0 \text{ to } 10)$

g $y = 8.4 \times 10^{-0.42t}$ $\qquad$ $t(0 \text{ to } 2)$

h $y = 9.7 \times 10^{-0.42t}$ $\qquad$ $t(0 \text{ to } 2)$

PART II

Applications of the Slide Rule
to Various Fields

The examples and problems of Part I are synthetic in several respects. Algebraic formulas are avoided to a large extent in Chapters 1 and 2, so that the reader unfamiliar with algebra can profit from that portion. Algebraic formulas with particular numerical values for the letter symbols are a necessary part of some applications. As another synthetic feature, the exponents in Chapter 4 are a single number, not a complex of numbers which must be reduced before proceeding with the exponential operation.

The examples of Part II demonstrate that the practical computations of business, science, and engineering are not always so conveniently presented to the computer, even though these examples are simplified in several respects.

Each problem is introduced by a word or phrase indicating the field of practice it represents and a brief statement of its nature. The algebraic formula and the units of the quantities are also given except for the very simple problems. In addition, several sets of numerical data are given as a means for providing practical calculation exercises. The answer to the first set of numerical data is given; for many of the problems the numerical calculation for this first set of data is shown along with suggestions for using the slide rule in its solution.

In practical work, problems seldom are given as a formula requiring merely substitution of numbers in it as is the case here. The more common problem situation requires careful analysis as well as numerical operations.

Even after the correct rational or empirical formula is determined, the computer must select the appropriate units and conversion factors. This step also has been given for the problems of Part II in order to focus attention on the slide rule operations.

Within each chapter, the examples are arranged in the order of the related Part I chapter: products and quotients, simple powers and roots, trigonometric functions, exponents or logarithms.

Chapter

5

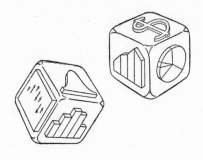

BUSINESS, FINANCE, AND STATISTICS

The problems in this chapter are intended to show a few examples only. An endless number of problems in accounting ratios, turnover, and interest could be prepared. In statistics, also, the handful of examples is a fraction of the possibilities; a statistical handbook[1] lists 434 formulas.

Comments are given with a few of the problems. Generally, the calculations are worked out for the first set of numerical data as an example. Problems are arranged in the order of the chapters of Part I with which they correspond. Several sets of numerical data are given in parentheses, arranged in indicated order.

5.1. Division and Multiplication. PROBLEM 5.1A. *Accounting.* The accounting ratio: Current Ratio = Current Assets/Current Liabilities.

Data: (Assets; Liabilities); (35,600; 15,400); (4850; 1970); (745; 365); (5900; 2775)

Example: Ratio = 35,600/15,400 = 2.31

PROBLEM 5.1B. *Accounting.* The ratio of net profit to net sales, expressed as per cent is: $R = 100 \times \text{Profit/Sales}$.

Data: (Profit; Sales; R); (720; 12,200; R); (P; 4200; 8.4); (13,600; S; 6.7); (61,500; 705,500; R)

Example: $R = 100 \times 720/12,200 = 5.90$

Cancellation of 100 with two zeros in the denominator simplifies decimal point placement.

---

[1] Dunlap, Jack W. and Albert K. Kurtz, *Handbook of Statistical Nomographs Tables and Formulas*, pages 103–140. New York: World Book Co., 1932.

PROBLEM 5.1C. *Investment.* The earning rate on an investment, as per cent, is given by: Earning (%) = 100 Dividend/Cost.

Data: (Cost; Dividend; Earning); ($5250; $341; E); ($11,750; D; 4.8%); (C; 192; 6.9%); ($420; $26; E).

Example: $E = 100 \times 341/5250 = 6.50\%$

PROBLEM 5.1D. *Business.* For straight line depreciation, and neglecting removal cost and salvage value: $D = I/l$; or $d = 100/l$ where I is investment in dollars, l is service life in years, d is annual depreciation in per cent, and D is depreciation in dollars per year.

Data: (I; l; D; d); ($250; 8 yrs.; D; d); ($3600; l; D; 3%); (I; 25 yrs.; $240; d); ($48,000; 42 yrs.; D; d)

Example: $d = 100/8 = 12.5$; $D = 250/8 = \$31.25$

PROBLEM 5.1E. *Business.* Annual turnover of merchandise is defined as cost of goods sold per year divided by average inventory, or

$$T = \frac{I_b + P - I_e}{(I_b + I_e)/2}$$

where I's are beginning and ending inventories, and P is purchases, all in dollars for the year.

Data: (I_b; I_e; P; T); (77,000; 63,000; 417,000; T); (4300; 7500; P; 3.4); (1250; 2140; 18,000; T); (500; I_e; 3400; 6.3)

Example: $T = (77 + 417 - 63)/(77 + 63)0.5 = 431/70 = 6.16$

Practice in algebraic manipulation is associated with the last set of values in which the ending inventory to attain a particular turnover is sought.

PROBLEM 5.1F. *Insurance.* If an annual insurance policy is cancelled pro rata before expiration, the premium returnable is

$$P = \frac{P_a d}{365} \quad \text{(dollars)}$$

where d is number of days before expiration and P_a is annual premium in dollars.

Data: (P_a; d); ($75; 160); ($42; 36); ($127; 205); ($67; 99).

Example: $P = 75 \times 160/365 = (73 + 2)160/365 = 160(1/5 + 2/365)$
$= \$32 + \$0.88 = \$32.88$

More accurate result is obtained if the number of days is factored into two parts as shown, and mental arithmetic is used for $160 \times 1/5$.

PROBLEM 5.1G. *Business.* The resultant price after a series of discounts is

$$P = P_e(1 - d_1)(1 - d_2)(1 - d_3) \text{ etc.} \qquad \text{(dollars)}$$

where P_e is list price and the d's are discounts expressed as decimals.

Data: $(d_1; d_2; d_3; P_e)$; (30%; 10%; 0%; $540); (20%; 10%; 5%; $860); (40%; 2%; 0%; $42); (25%; 15%; 5%; $67).

Example: $P = \$540(0.7)(0.9) = \$340$

The C, CI, and D scales enable one to perform the example calculation in one slide setting, Art. 1.18.

PROBLEM 5.1H. *Business.* Retail price per unit, if mark up and lot quantity cost are known, is

$$P_u = \frac{C_q}{q(1 - m)}$$

where q is quotation quantity (dozen, gross, and so on), m is mark up as a ratio, C_q is cost in dollars for the quotation quantity.

Data: $(C_q; q; m; P_u)$; ($167; 12; 37%; P_u); ($580; 144; m; $5.95); ($C_q$; 12; 48%; $5.95); ($1.75; 1; 40%; P_u).

Example: $P_u = 167/(12 \times 0.63) = \$22.10$

As in Problem 5.1G, it is possible to solve these examples in one slide setting.

PROBLEM 5.1I. *Statistics.* One form of the Spearman-Brown formula is

$$n = \frac{r_n(1 - r_1)}{r_1(1 - r_n)}$$

where r_1 is reliability of a test, r_n is desired reliability, n is number of times longer the test must be.

Data: $(r_1; r_n; n)$; (0.37; 0.52; n); (0.73; 0.85; n); (0.80; 0.62; n); (0.78; r_n; 3.5).

Example: $n = \dfrac{0.52(1 - 0.37)}{0.37(1 - 0.52)} = 1.85$

5.2. Simple Powers and Roots. The problems in this article may be solved with LogLog scales, or simple power and root scales as described in Chapter 2.

PROBLEM 5.2A. *Statistics.* The standard error of the mean is

$$\theta_m = \frac{\theta}{\sqrt{N}}$$

where θ is standard deviation of the distribution and N is number of observations.

Data: $(\theta; N; \theta_m)$; $(4.35; 500; \theta_m)$; $(8.72; 150; \theta_m)$; $(3.86; N; 0.052)$; $(7.12; 1200; \theta_m)$.

Example: $\theta_m = 4.35/\sqrt{500} = 0.195$

PROBLEM 5.2B. *Statistics.* The standard deviation of the sum or difference of raw scores when the data are uncorrelated is

$$\theta = \sqrt{\theta_1{}^2 + \theta_2{}^2}$$

Data: $(\theta_1; \theta_2)$; $(3.2; 1.65)$; $(1.85; 4.3)$; $(2.65; 2.45)$; $(6.75; 1.35)$

Example: $\theta = \sqrt{3.2^2 + 1.65^2} = 3.60$

PROBLEM 5.2C. *Statistics.* The standard error of the Pearson product moment coefficient of correlation is

$$\theta_r = \frac{(1 - r^2)}{\sqrt{N}}$$

where r is the Pearson coefficient and N is number of cases or observations.

Data: $(r; N)$; $(0.37; 160)$; $(0.26; 120)$; $(0.74; 490)$; $(0.57; 360)$

Example: $\theta_r = (1 - 0.37^2)/\sqrt{160} = 0.863/12.65 = 0.0684$

PROBLEM 5.2D. *Statistics.* The geometric mean of a set of n numbers is given by

$$d = \sqrt[n]{d_1 \times d_2 \times d_3 \cdots d_n}$$

Data: Several examples for $n = 6$ are given. $(5; 7; 9; 11; 13; 15)$; $(34; 35; 36; 37; 38; 39)$; $(15; 25; 35; 45; 55; 65)$; $(3; 32; 56; 70; 121; 460)$

Example: $d = \sqrt[6]{5 \times 7 \times 9 \times 11 \times 13 \times 15} = \sqrt[6]{675,000} = 9.37$

5.3. Trigonometric Calculations. Trigonometric functions are rare in calculations directly associated with business, finance, or statistics.   One example is shown.

PROBLEM 5.3A. *Statistics.* The corrected rank correlation coefficient is

$$r_p = 2 \sin \frac{\pi}{6} P$$

Data: (P); (0.14); (0.23); (0.52); (0.75)

Example: $r_p = 2 \sin \dfrac{\pi \times 0.14}{6} = 2 \sin 0.0733 = 0.1464$

The angle in radians must be converted to degrees for slide rule setting.

5.4. Logarithmic and Exponential Calculations. PROBLEM 5.4A. *Statistics.* Ordinates for the normal curve are given by

$$y = \frac{n}{\theta \sqrt{2\pi}} e^{\frac{-x^2}{2\theta^2}}$$

Data: Assuming $n = 1$ and $\theta = 1$, calculate y for $x = 0.3; 1.5; 1.64; 2.6$

Example: $y = \dfrac{e^{\frac{-0.09}{2}}}{\sqrt{2\pi}} = \dfrac{0.956}{2.506} = 0.382$

PROBLEM 5.4B. *Finance.* The amount of P dollars for n years at r rate of interest compounded at t years interval is given by

$$A = P(1 + tr)^{n/t} \qquad \text{(dollars)}$$

where r is expressed as a decimal.

Data: $(P; t; r; n; A); (4000; 1; 0.045; 15; A); (2500; 0.5; 0.03; n; 3000);$
$(P; 0.25; 0.035; 12; 1300); (1000; 0.5; r; 10; 2000)$

Example: $A = 4000(1 + 0.045)^{15} = 4000 \times 1.935 = 7740$

PROBLEM 5.4C. *Finance.* Payments to a sinking fund in constant amounts for a depreciation reserve are

$$P = \frac{rA}{(1 + r)^n - 1}$$

where r is annual interest rate as a decimal, n is number of annual payments, A is the amount to be accumulated, and P is annual payment.

Data: $(r; n; A; P); (0.045; 15; \$4500; P); (0.05; 10; A; \$250); (0.035; 20;$
$\$13,500; P); (0.04; n; \$5000; \$500)$

Example: $P = \dfrac{0.045 \times 4500}{(1 + 0.045)^{15} - 1} = \dfrac{202.5}{0.935} = \$216.50$

PROBLEM 5.4D. *Finance.* The amount of equal periodic payments required to amortize a debt is given by

$$rA = P\left[1 - \frac{1}{(1 + r)^n}\right]$$

where A is the amount of the debt, n is number of payments, r is interest rate for payment interval as a decimal.

Data: $(r; n; A; P); (0.045; 15; \$4500; P); (0.055; 12; A; \$400); (0.03; 10;$
$\$8000; P); (r; 8; \$2200; \$240)$

Example: $4500 \times 0.045 = P[1 - (1.045)^{-15}]$
$P = 4500 \times 0.045/0.483 = \$419$

PROBLEM 5.4E.   *Finance*.   The equation of Problem 5.4D is equally applicable for monthly payments.

Data: $(r; n; A; P)$; $(0.06/12; 20 \text{ mo}; \$250; P)$; $(0.05/12; 18 \text{ mo}; \$175; P)$;
$(0.06/12; n; \$500; \$20)$

Example: $250 \times 0.005 = P[1 - 1.005^{-20}]$
$P = 1.25/(1 - 0.905) = \$13.15$

Chapter

6

CHEMISTRY AND PHYSICS

Scientific work in general is represented by problems selected from two principal fields. The terms physics or chemistry describe all or most of these examples.

6.1. Division and Multiplication. PROBLEM 6.1A. *Mechanics.* If a load is to be lifted by a differential hoist having a mechanical advantage of 16, what force must be exerted neglecting friction?

Data: (Loads); (2735 lb; 3720 lb; 1560 lb; 3.7 tons)

Example: 2735/16 = 171 lb

PROBLEM 6.1B. *Expansion of Metals.* The mean coefficients of linear expansion per degree F are: 0.0000096 for copper; 0.0000128 for aluminum; 0.0000069 for steel.

Data: (material; length, ft; temp change, °F; length change, ft); (copper; 620; 120; _____); (steel; 125; _____; 0.175); (aluminum; 1200; 90; _____); (copper; 860; _____; 0.95)

$$\begin{matrix} -6 & +2 & +2 & -2 \end{matrix}$$
Example: $9.6 \times 6.20 \times 1.20 = 71.4 = 0.714$

If the CI, C, and D scales are used, one slide setting is sufficient for this example.

PROBLEM 6.1C. *Sound.* If sound travels 1080 feet per second and several crashes of thunder are timed after the flash with a stop watch, find the distances to each of the strokes if the times are: 4.5 sec; 7.2 sec; 8.5 sec; 9.4 sec.

Example: $1080 \times 4.5 = 4860$ ft.

PROBLEM 6.1D. *Thermometry.* Temperatures in °F and °C are related by

$$F = 1.8C + 32$$

where F is Fahrenheit temperature and C is Centigrade temperature. Find temperatures on the other scale for the following melting points of metals: tin 232°C; zinc 419°C; copper 1981°F; lead 628°F.

Example: $F = 1.8 \times 232 + 32 = 450°$

PROBLEM 6.1E. *Radio.* For short wave calculations it is often convenient to determine wave lengths in inches from

$$\lambda = 11.8 \times \frac{10^9}{f} \qquad \text{(in.)}$$

where f is frequency in cycles per sec. Determine λ or f for: 2.95″; 2500 mega-cycles; 1.26″; 6000 mega-cycles.

Example: $f = 11.8 \times 10^9/2.95 = 4.00 \times 10^9$, or 4000 mega-cycles per sec.

PROBLEM 6.1F. *Electricity.* The capacity of a parallel plate condenser is given by

$$C = \frac{kA}{4\pi d} \qquad \text{(e.s.u.)}$$

where k is dielectric constant; A is area of plate in sq cm; d is distance between plates in cm.

Data: $(k; A; d; C)$; (3.7; 540; 0.052; C); (4.8; 165; d; 1520); (k; 720; 0.077; 1680); (1; A; 1.6; 535)

Example: $C = (3.7 \times 540)/(4\pi \times 0.052) = 3060$

One less slide operation is possible if π-folded scales are available.

PROBLEM 6.1G. *Electricity.* Ohm's law is

$$E = RI$$

where R is resistance in ohms, I is current in amps, E is in volts.

Data: $(E; R; I)$; (110; R; 4.7); (E; 5920; 0.675); (15,000; 465; I); (E; 1752; 1.31)

Example: $R = 110/4.7 = 23.4$

PROBLEM 6.1H. *Electricity.* Several inductive reactances in parallel have an equivalent reactance, X, given by

$$\frac{1}{X} = \frac{1}{2\pi f L_1} + \frac{1}{2\pi f L_2} + \frac{1}{2\pi f L_3} \cdots$$

where f is frequency of alternating current in cycles per sec, L's are inductances in henrys, X is in ohms.

Data: $(f; L_1; L_2; L_3; X)$; $(60; 0.3; 0.13; 0.072; X)$; $(400; L_1; 0.076; 0.175; 155)$; $(60; 0.45; 0.67; L_3; 82)$; $(f; 0.038; 0.092; 0.071; 490)$

Example: $2 \times \pi \times \dfrac{60}{X} = \dfrac{1}{0.3} + \dfrac{1}{0.13} + \dfrac{1}{0.072} = 24.93$
$X = 120\pi/24.73 = 15.12$

If scales folded at π are available, the multiplication by π may be performed as shown in Fig. 1.29.

PROBLEM 6.1I. *Electricity.* The equivalent resistance for several resistances in parallel, Fig. 6.1, is given by

$$\frac{1}{R} = \frac{1}{R_1} + \frac{1}{R_2} + \frac{1}{R_3} + \cdots$$

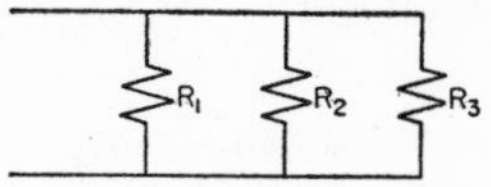

where R's are in ohms. Assume three resistors in parallel for the problems.

Fig. 6.1. Resistors in Parallel

Data: $(R_1; R_2; R_3; R)$; $(27; 5; 84; R)$; $(R_1; 11.5; 42; 8.7)$; $(162; 137; R_3; 67)$; $(3.72; 3.10; R_3; 2.15)$

Example: $\dfrac{1}{R} = \dfrac{1}{27} + \dfrac{1}{5} + \dfrac{1}{84}$
$= 0.0371 + 0.2 + 0.0119 = 0.249$
$R = 1/0.249 = 4.016$

The four digit answer may be obtained by partial mental operation as described in Art. 1.15.

PROBLEM 6.1J. *Gas Law.* The perfect gas equation

$$\frac{P_1 V_1}{T_1} = \frac{P_2 V_2}{T_2}$$

contains six quantities, and if five are known the remaining one can be calculated. In the equation, T_1 and T_2 are absolute temperatures; P_1 and P_2 are absolute pressures; V_1 and V_2 are volumes. The given data and the required answers may be on other temperature scales or the pressures may be gauge pressures. Also, each pair of quantities may be in any appropriate units, but must be in the same units.

Data: $(P_1; V_1; t_1; P_2; V_2; t_2)$; $(260; 5.8; 20°C; P_2; 8.6; 80°C)$; $(190; 1.7; 820°F; 240; V_2; 240°F)$; $(360; 9.8; t_1; 85; 18.6; 400°C)$; $(P_1; 0.85; 370°F; 480; 1.1; 560°F)$; $(25; 5.1; 320°C; 120; 2.3; t_2)$. (Given pressures in psia, volumes in cu ft.)

Example: $\dfrac{260 \times 5.8}{273 + 20} = \dfrac{P_2 \times 8.6}{273 + 80}$

$$P_2 = \dfrac{260 \times 5.8 \times 353}{293 \times 8.6} = 211$$

6.2. Simple Powers and Roots. PROBLEM 6.2A. *Strength of Materials.* The average stress in a round rod subjected to tension is

$$S = \frac{4P}{\pi D^2} \qquad \text{(lb per sq in.)}$$

where P is load in lb; D is diam in in.

Data: $(P; D; S)$; $(6500; 0.46; S)$; $(42,000; D; 125,000)$; $(P; 0.875; 32,000)$; $(13,400; 2.25; S)$

Example: $S = \dfrac{4 \times 6500}{\pi \times 0.46^2} = 39,200$

Mental multiplication of 4×6500 may speed up solution.

PROBLEM 6.2B. *Electricity.* Power in a d.c. electric circuit is given by

$$P = I^2 R = \frac{E^2}{R} \qquad \text{(watts)}$$

where I is current in amps; R is resistance in ohms; E is in volts.

Data: $(I; R; E; P)$; $(75; 7.65; E; P)$; $(8.6; R; E; 746)$; $(I; 4.6; 120; P)$; $(I; R; 110; 3400)$

Example: $P = 75^2 \times 7.65 = 43,000$; $E = 573$

PROBLEM 6.2C. *Chemistry.* The solubility product constant K_{sp} of a salt is a measure of the solubility of the salt. K_{sp} for salts of the type AB_2 (PbI_2 is an example) may be calculated from

$$K_{sp} = C_A C_B^2$$

where C represents the molar concentration of the ion represented by the subscript.

Data: $(C_A; C_B; K_{sp}; \text{Salt})$; $(0.00152; 0.00304; K_{sp}; PbI_2)$; $(8 \times 10^{-7}; 1.6 \times 10^{-6}; K_{sp}; Co(OH)_2)$; $(C_A; 7.8 \times 10^{-2}; 2.4 \times 10^{-4}; PbCl_2)$; $(0.92 \times 10^{-4}; C_B; 3.2 \times 10^{-11}; Mg(OH)_2)$

Example: $K_{sp} = 0.00152 \times 0.00304^2 = 1.4 \times 10^{-10}$

PROBLEM 6.2D. *Chemistry.* The strength of acids depends upon the concentration of hydrogen ions present. In dilute solutions the ionization constant K_i is a measure of the relative strength of the acid. K_i for acids of the type HX, acetic acid ($H - C_2H_3O_2$) for example, may be

calculated from

$$K_i = \frac{C_H{}^2}{(1 - C_H)}$$

where C represents the molar concentration of the H ion.

Data: $(C_H; K_i; \text{Acid})$; $(0.00134; K_i; \text{acetic})$; $(0.0065; K_i; \text{nitrous})$; $(C_H; 5.4 \times 10^{-4}; \text{benzoic})$; $(C_H; 7 \times 10^{-10}; \text{hydrocyanic})$

Example: $K_i = (1.34 \times 10^{-3})^2/(1 - 1.34 \times 10^{-3}) = 1.82 \times 10^{-6}$

6.3. Trigonometric Calculations. PROBLEM 6.3A. *Physical Chemistry.* In the study of X-ray data on crystals, Bragg's Law is

$$2d \sin \theta = n\lambda$$

where d is distance between atom-bearing planes in Angstroms, n is order of reflection of the X-rays, λ is wave length of the X-rays in Angstroms, and θ is the angle of incidence of the X-rays.

Data: $n = 1$, $\lambda = 1.54$. Find d for $\theta = 9°52'$; $6°00'$; $25°11'$; $3°15'$

Example: $d = \dfrac{1.52}{2 \sin 9°52'} = 4.49$

Set hairline to 1.54 on D
Place 9°52' on S beneath hairline
At 2 on CI read 4.49 on D

PROBLEM 6.3B. *Electricity.* Alternating current impedances are commonly expressed in one of the forms

$$R + jX, \text{ or } Z\underline{/\theta}$$

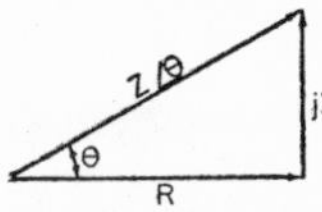

where, as shown in Fig. 6.2,

$$\theta = \frac{\tan^{-1} X}{R}; \quad Z = \sqrt{R^2 + X^2}$$

Fig. 6.2. Impedance Vectors

Transformation from one form to the other is frequently needed, which calls for solution of a right triangle.

Data: $(R; X; Z; \theta)$; $(17.8; 42.5; Z; \theta)$; $(R; X; 8.50; 52°)$; $(7.2; -35.0; Z; \theta)$; $(R; X; 10.9; 37°)$

Example: $\tan \theta = 42.5/17.8 = 2.38$, or $Z = 46.1\underline{/67.25°}$

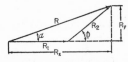

Fig. 6.3. Composition of Force Vectors

PROBLEM 6.3C. *Mechanics.* Resolution of forces into components along particular lines and the determination of the resultant of several forces occur frequently in mechanics. The transformation is essentially a triangle problem, Fig. 6.3.

Data: $(R_1; R_2; \phi; \alpha; R)$; $(1.75; 0.54; 62°; \alpha; R)$; $(13.4; R_2; \phi; 42°; 26.5)$;
$(R_1; 3.8; 125°; 32°; R)$; $(R_1; R_2; 110°; 40°; 5.8)$

Example: $R_x = 0.54 \cos 62° = 0.254$
$R_y = 0.54 \sin 62° = 0.477$
$\alpha = \tan^{-1} 0.477/2.004 = 13.4°$
$$R = 2.004 + \frac{0.477^2}{4.008} = 2.061$$

PROBLEM 6.3D. *Light.* The index of refraction is a function of material and color

$$n = \frac{\sin I}{\sin R}$$

where I is the angle of incidence and R is angle of refraction.

Data: $(I; R; n)$; $(60°; 40.5°; n)$; $(I; 35°; 1.57)$; $(55°; R; 1.96)$; $(75°; 46.5°; n)$

Example: $n = \sin 60°/\sin 40.5°$, or $n/\sin 60° = 1/\sin 40.5°$; $n = 1.33$

6.4. Logarithmic and Exponential Calculations. PROBLEM 6.4A. *Atmospheric Pressure.* Barometric pressure at different elevations is given by

$$P = 29.92 \times e^{-0.0384h}$$

where h is elevation in thousands of feet.

Data: $(h; P)$; $(8.2; P)$; $(21; P)$; $(h; 17.6)$; $(h; 14.5)$

Example: $P = 29.92e^{-0.0384 \times 8.2} = 29.92 \times 0.73 = 21.8$

PROBLEM 6.4B. *Physical Chemistry.* The pH of a solution and the activity, A_{H^+}, of the hydrogen ion are related by the equation

$$pH = - \log A_{H^+}$$

Data: $(pH; A_{H^+})$; $(4.35; A_{H^+})$; $(3.75; A_{H^+})$; $(6.10; A_{H^+})$; $(pH; 0.0032)$; $(pH; 0.00056)$; $(pH; 0.000000082)$

Example: $\log A_{H^+} = -4.35$; $\log \dfrac{1}{A_{H^+}} = 4.35$

Set to the mantissa, 0.35, on L   Set to 0.35 on D
        $+4$ $1/A_{H^+}$ appears on N_3
Read 2.24 on D for $1/A_{H^+}$ -4
On DI or on CI aligned read A_{H^+} appears on $1/N_3$ as 0.446
    0.446

PROBLEM 6.4C. *Physical Chemistry.* The pressures and temperatures of boiling water are related by the equation

$$\ln \frac{P_2}{P_1} = \frac{\Delta H_v (T_2 - T_1)}{R T_2 T_1}$$

where R is 1.987 cal per mole-deg ΔH_v is 9720 cal per mole at 760 mm pressure, T_1 and T_2 are in degrees K.

Data: $(P_2; T_2)$; (650 mm; T_2); (580 mm; T_2); (810 mm; T_2); (550 mm; T_2); $(P_2; 365°K)$; $(P_2; 368°K)$; $(P_2; 379°K)$; $(P_2; 360°K)$

Example: $\ln \dfrac{650}{760} = \dfrac{9720(T_2 - 273)}{1.987 \times T_2 \times 273}$

this reduces to

$$1.00875 T_2 = 273$$

or since for numbers close to 1, the reciprocal is given closely by

$$\frac{1}{(1 + a)} = 1 - a \qquad (a < 0.01)$$

and

$$T_2 = 273 - 0.00875 \times 273 = 270.6$$

PROBLEM 6.4D. *Mechanics.* The maximum belt tension ratio for a pulley and belt, Fig. 6.4, is given by

$$\frac{T_2}{T_1} = e^{u\theta}$$

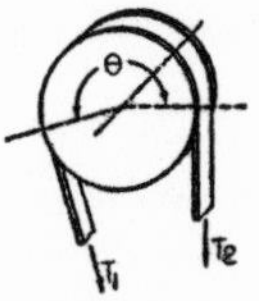

where u is coefficient of friction between pulley and belt, θ is angle of contact in radians; T_2 and T_1 are belt tensions in like units.

Fig. 6.4.
Belt Tension
Diagram

Data: $(u; \theta; T_1; T_2)$; (0.304; 100°; 65 lb; T_2); (0.24; θ; 175 lb; 220 lb); (0.37; 540°; T_1; 68 lb); (u; 810°; 56 lb; 410 lb)

Example: $\dfrac{T_2}{65} = e^{\frac{0.304 \times 100°}{57.3°}} = e^{0.535} = 1.70$

$$T_2 = 1.70 \times 65 = 110.5 \text{ lb}$$

PROBLEM 6.4E. *Physical Chemistry.* The free energy change, ΔF, for the reaction

$$H_2PO_4^- \rightleftharpoons HPO_4 = +H^+$$

is given by

$$F = -RT \ln K$$

where R is 1.987 cal per mole-degree, T is degrees Kelvin.

Data: $(\Delta F; T; K)$; (18,000 cal; 298°K; K); (16,500 cal; 310°K; K); (ΔF; 360°K; 2.5×10^{-12}); (ΔF; 280°K; 4.5×10^{-12})

Example: $\ln K = \dfrac{-18,000}{1.987 \times 298} = -30.4$

$\ln \dfrac{1}{K} = 30.4$

The LogLog scales seldom include $+30$ or -30, but since

$$\log \dfrac{1}{K} = 0.434 \ln \dfrac{1}{K}$$

$$\log \dfrac{1}{K} = 0.434 \times 30.4 = 13.2$$

$$\dfrac{1}{K} = 1.583 \times 10^{13}; \ K = 0.637 \times 10^{-13}$$

Chapter

7

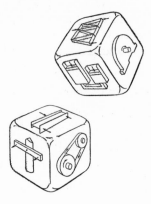

ENGINEERING

The problems in this chapter are not necessarily a representative sample of engineering applications. They have been selected: (a) to show methods of attack on some of the more difficult or complex slide rule calculations; (b) to indicate the variety of fields of usefulness; and (c) to provide problems for practice which are not merely numbers, but have physical meaning associated with them.

Descriptions of the setting, method for placing the decimal point, and other comments are given with some of the problems. Generally, and as an example, the calculations are worked out for the first set of numerical data. Problems are arranged in the order of the chapters of Part I to which they correspond.

7.1. Division and Multiplication. PROBLEM 7.1A. *Fluid Mechanics, Hydraulics.* The pressure of water at various depths, H in ft, is given by

$$p = Hd \qquad \text{(lb per sq ft)}$$

where d is density in lb per cu ft, or 62.4 for fresh water. Find the water pressure at the foot of a dam if the depth of water is: 730 ft; 550 ft; 250 ft; 45 ft. Determine pressures in lb per sq in.

Example: $P = \dfrac{62.4 \times 730}{144} = 316$ (lb per sq in)

PROBLEM 7.1B. *Fluid Mechanics, Hydraulics.* The force on a surface submerged in a liquid is given by

$$F = dHA$$

157

where d is density of liquid in lb per cu ft, H is depth in ft to center of gravity of surface, and A is area of surface in sq ft. If the density of sea water is 64 lb per cu ft, find the force tending to crush a submarine door of 2.25 sq ft submerged to depths of: 135 ft; 220 ft; 160 ft; 120 ft.

Example: $F = 64 \times 135 \times 2.25 = 19{,}400$ lb. Multiplying three factors in one setting of the slide is possible using CI, C, and D scales.

> Set hairline to 64 on D
> Place 135 on CI beneath hairline
> At 2.25 on C read answer on D

PROBLEM 7.1C. *Machine Tools.* The surface speed of a flywheel, grinder, pulley or other rotating device is given by

$$L = \pi DS$$

where D is diam in ft, S is rpm, and L is in ft per min.

Data: $(D; S; L)$; $(1.5; 37.5; L)$; $(D; 875; 270)$; $(0.67; 1800; L)$; $(0.167; S; 5000)$

Example: $L = \pi \times 1.5 \times 375 = 1765$. If π-folded scales are available

> Set left index of C to 1.5
> At 375 on C find 1.5×375 on D (560 approx.)
> π times the product appears on DF

PROBLEM 7.1D. *Thermodynamics.* The efficiency of a thermal process is given by

$$n = \frac{2545hp}{Q}$$

where the 2545 is in Btu per hp-hr, Q is Btu input per hr, and hp is horsepower output.

Data: $(Q; hp)$; $(17{,}450; 2.2)$; $(6280; 0.8)$; $(9800; 1.3)$; $(13{,}000; 1.8)$; $(750{,}000; 11.7)$

Example: $n = 2545 \times 2.2/17{,}450 = 0.321$, or 32.1%

PROBLEM 7.1E. *Mechanics.* The maximum stress at any section of a uniform beam is given by

$$s = \frac{Mc}{I}$$

where M is bending moment at the section in in-lb, c is distance from center of gravity to extreme fiber in in., I is moment of inertia in in.[4]

Data: $(M; c; I; s)$; $(41{,}000; 6; 15.7; s)$; $(M; 3.75; 24.5; 12{,}000)$; $(8400; c; 1.75; 8000)$; $(62{,}500; 5.7; 35.6; s)$

Example: $s = \dfrac{41,000 \times 6}{15.7} = 15,650$

PROBLEM 7.1F. *Machine Tools.* The time of operation for a cut on a milling machine is given by

$$T = \frac{L}{R \times f}$$

where L is length of cut in in., f is feed in in. per rev, R is rpm, and T is in min.

Data: $(L; R; f; T)$; $(13.5; 125; 0.07; T)$; $(8.5; 625; 0.03; T)$; $(16.0; R; 0.055; 2.5)$; $(4.5; 425; f; 0.8)$

Example: $T = 13.5/(125 \times 0.07) = 1.54$

> Set hairline to 13.5 on D
> Place 125 on C beneath hairline
> At 0.07 on CI read answer on D

PROBLEM 7.1G. *Fluid Mechanics.* The power required to elevate a liquid, neglecting pipe friction, is

$$hp = \frac{8.33 \times GHS_g}{33,000 \ n} \qquad \text{(horsepower)}$$

where 8.33 lb is the weight of a gallon of water, S_g is the specific gravity of liquid being pumped, H is height of pumping in ft, G is rate of pumping in gal per min, and n is pump efficiency.

Data: $(G; H; S_g; hp)$; $(5000; 75; 1.03; hp)$; $(3200; 165; 1; hp)$; $(G; 42; 1; 400)$; $(650; 15; 1.2: hp)$; $(G; 250; 1; 600)$; $(1200; H; 1; 200)$

Example: $hp = (8.33 \times 5000 \times 75 \times 1.03)/(33,000 \times 0.7) = 139$. An operating sequence which requires minimum slide movement is

$$\frac{8.33_\text{D} \quad 75_\text{C} \quad 5_\text{CF}}{0.7_\text{C} \quad 33_\text{C}} \times 1.03_\text{CIF} = 139_\text{DF}$$

PROBLEM 7.1H. *Electricity.* The resistance of a conductor is given by

$$R = \frac{rL}{A}$$

where r is resistivity of the material in ohms per circular mil-ft, L is length in ft, A is area in circular mils

Data: $(L; A; R; r)$; $(650; 16,500; R; 10.8)$; $(1100; 105,500; R; 17.6)$; $(4800; 211,600; 0.245; r)$; $(L; 4100; 5.4; 10.8)$; $(1800; A; 1.21; 17.6)$

Example: $R = 10.8 \times 650/16,500 = 0.426$. (Copper wire resistivity is 10.8 at 25°C; aluminum wire resistivity is 17.6 at 25°C.)

PROBLEM 7.1I. *Electricity.* Area of a conductor in circular mils is equal to the diameter of solid round conductor in thousandths of inches squared. Equivalent cross-sectional area of rectangular conductor in circular mils is

$$A = \frac{4}{\pi} W \times D$$

where W and D are width and depth in thousandths of an in. Find circular mil equivalent for square and rectangular bars as follows: 0.375″ × 0.5″; 0.375″ × 3″; 0.25″ × 2.5″; 0.625″ × 0.625″.

Example: $A = \frac{4}{\pi} \times 375 \times 500 = 239{,}000$

> Set hairline to 500 on DF
> Place 375 on CI beneath the hairline
> The product appears on DF at the index of CI as 187.5×10^3
> Division by π appears on D at the index of CI
> To multiply by 4 set hairline to 4 on C and read on D

PROBLEM 7.1J. *Machine Design.* The coefficient of friction for a lubricated bearing is given by the empirical equation

$$f = 0.002 + \frac{473ZND}{10^{10}PC}$$

where Z is absolute viscosity in poises, N is journal speed in rpm, D is bearing diam in., P is unit bearing pressure, lb per sq in., C is clearance in.

Data: $(Z; N; D; P; C)$; (22.6; 1800; 4.0; 406; 0.004); (14.5; 3600; 2.6; 500; 0.003); (12.4; 3000; 3.75; 375; 0.004); (56.0; 900; 6.25; 520; 0.006)

Example:
$$f = 0.002 + \frac{473 \times 22.6 \times 1800 \times 4.0}{10^{10} \times 406 \times 0.004}$$

$$ +1 \quad +1 \quad +3$$

$$= 0.002 + \frac{4.73 \times 2.26 \times 1.8 \times 4}{1.0 \times 4.06 \times 4.0}$$

$$ +10 \quad +2 \quad -3$$

$$= 0.002 + 0.000473 = 0.002473$$

PROBLEM 7.1K. *Electrical Engineering.* The reactance for an alternating current series circuit is given by

$$X = 2\pi fL - \frac{1}{2\pi fC} \qquad \text{(ohms)}$$

where f is frequency in cycles per sec, L is inductance in henrys, C is capacitance in farads.

Data: $(f; L; C; X)$; $(400; 0.0017; 0.00078; X)$; $(60; L; 0.00095; 0.45)$;
$(12,000; 0.003; C; 8)$; $(f; 0.0024; 0.0005; X)$

Example: $X = 2\pi \times 400 \times 0.0017 - \dfrac{1}{2\pi \times 400 \times 0.00078} = 4.27 - 0.51$

PROBLEM 7.1L. *Electrical Engineering.* For a resonant circuit, X in the equation of Problem 7.1K becomes zero, or

$$2\pi fL = \frac{1}{2\pi fC}$$

Data: $(f; L; C)$; $(400; L; 0.0000085)$; $(60; 0.35; C)$; $(f; 0.0016; 0.000062)$;
$(5600; 0.00032; C)$

Example: $800\pi \times L = \dfrac{1}{(800\pi \times 0.0000085)}$

$$L = \frac{1}{(0.8 \times 10^3\pi)^2 \times 8.5 \times 10^{-6}} = \overset{-2}{1.87}$$

If f is solved for as in the third set of data, square root is involved; such is the nature of some of the problems in the next article.

7.2. Simple Powers and Roots.

The problems in this article may be solved with LogLog scales, or simple power and root scales as described in Chapter 2.

PROBLEM 7.2A. *Thermodynamics.* The maximum velocity of vapor flow, V_2, in a nozzle is given by

$$\frac{V_2{}^2}{2g} = 778(h_1 - h_2)$$

where V_2 is in ft per sec, g is acceleration of gravity, 32.2 ft per sec^2, 778 is ft-lb per Btu, h_1 and h_2 are in Btu per lb.

Data: $(h_1; h_2; V_2)$; $(1257; 1107; V_2)$; $(h_1; 1050; 3000)$; $(1420; h_2; 3100)$;
$(1315; 1150; V_2)$

Example: $V_2{}^2 = 64.4 \times 778(1257 - 1107)$
$$\overset{+6}{= 50{,}200 \times 150 = 7.52}$$
$$\overset{+3}{V_2 = 2.74 = 2740}$$

PROBLEM 7.2B. *Structures.* The Euler formula for maximum buckling load on a column is

$$P = \frac{\pi^2 EI}{l^2} \qquad \text{(lb)}$$

where E is modulus of elasticity lb per sq in., I is moment of inertia in.^{4}, l is length of column, in in.

Data: $(E = 29 \times 10^6)$; $(I; l; P)$; $(16.72; 18'; P)$; $(I; 12'; 65,000)$; $(37.5; 22'; P)$; $(12.6; l; 38,000)$

Example: $P = \dfrac{\pi^2 \times 29 \times 10^6 \times 16.72}{(18 \times 12)^2} = 102,000$ lb

Column length in ft must be converted to in. Folded scales facilitate one multiplication by π.

PROBLEM 7.2C. *Thermodynamics.* The specific heat at constant pressure for CO_2 is given by the empirical equation

$$C_p = 16.2 - \frac{6530}{T} + \frac{1.41 \times 10^6}{T^2}$$

where T is degrees Rankine. Find C_p for the following temperatures: 700°R; 640°R; 930°R; 520°R

Example: $C_p = 16.2 - \dfrac{6530}{700} + \dfrac{1.41 \times 10^6}{0.7^2 \times 10^6}$
$= 16.2 - 9.33 + 2.88 = 9.75$

Decimal point position is simplified by writing $T = 700 = 0.7 \times 10^3$ for the last term.

If C_p were given and T sought, solution of a quadratic equation would be required.

PROBLEM 7.2D. *Railways and Highways.* The super-elevation of the outside rail on a railway curve is given by

$$e = \frac{dV^2}{gR}$$

where d is rail spacing, V is design speed of train ft per sec, R is radius of curve ft, g is acceleration of gravity. For highways, d is width of road.

Data: d for standard gauge railway is 4 ft 8 1/2 in., $g = 32.2$ ft/sec²; $(R; V; e)$; $(1400; 102.5; e)$; $(R; 58.7; 0.3)$; $(1800; V; 0.7)$; $(1200; 132; e)$

Example: $e = \dfrac{4.708 \times 102.5^2}{32.2 \times 1400} = 1.10$

PROBLEM 7.2E. *Bridges and Transmission Lines.* Suspension bridge cables and overhead electric transmission lines cables are sometimes assumed to hang in a parabolic curve, Fig. 7.1, for which

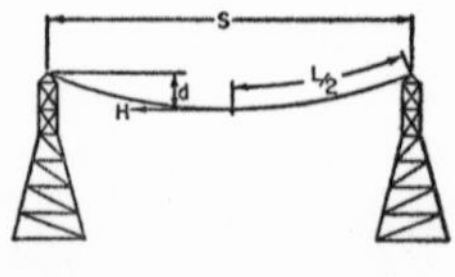

Fig. 7.1. Suspension Cable

$$d = \frac{WS^2}{8H}$$

where d is sag at mid-span below supports in ft; W is load per ft in lb, S is span in ft, H is horizontal tension lb.

Data: $(W; S; H; d)$; $(1.42; 1100; 12,000; d)$; $(2.45; 860; H; 21)$; $(1.82; S;$
8000; 5.7)$; $(0.85; 350; 6800; d)$

Example: $d = \dfrac{1.42 \times 1100^2}{8 \times 12,000} = 17.9$

PROBLEM 7.2F. *Bridges and Transmission Lines.* The length of
cable in Problem 7.2E is given by

$$L = S\left(1 + \frac{8}{3}\frac{d^2}{S^2} - \frac{32}{5}\frac{d^4}{S^4} + \cdots\right) \qquad \text{(ft)}$$

where the symbols have the same meaning as in Problem 7.2E.

Data: $(d; S)$; $(17.9; 1100)$; $(29; 960)$; $(50; 1000)$; $(7.5; 450)$

Example: $L = 1100\left(1 + \dfrac{8}{3} \times \dfrac{17.9^2}{1100^2} - \dfrac{32}{5} \times \dfrac{17.9^4}{1100^4}\right)$
$= 1100(1 + 0.0071 - ?)$
$= 1100.8$

The third term in the series is negligible when d/S is small, say less than
1/20, as it is for all of these problems.

PROBLEM 7.2G. *Machine Design.* The amplitude of vibration for a
load suspended on a spring is given by

$$y = \sqrt{\frac{W}{kg}V_0^2 + X_0^2} \qquad \text{(in.)}$$

where W is weight in lb, k is spring scale in lb per in., g is acceleration of
gravity in. per sec^2; V_0 is initial velocity in. per sec, X_0 is initial displace-
ment in in.

Data: $g = 386$ in./sec^2; $(W; k; V_0; X_0; y)$; $(52; 22; 75; 1.5; y)$; $(W; 15; 48;$
2.4; 5.2)$; $(27; k; 33; 1.8; 3.6)$; $(750; 80; 17; X_0; 1.8)$; $(13; 7; V_0;$
1.9; 7.4)$

Example: $y = \sqrt{\dfrac{52 \times 75^2}{22 \times 386} + 1.5^2} = \sqrt{34.5 + 2.25} = 6.06$

PROBLEM 7.2H. *Heat Transfer.* The Stefan-Boltzmann law for
black body radiation is

$$q = 0.174A\left(\frac{T}{100}\right)^4 \qquad \text{(Btu per sq ft)}$$

where A is radiation surface area sq ft, T is in degrees Rankine, and 0.174
is a natural constant.

Data: $(A; T; q)$; $(5.2; 1800°R; q)$; $(3.2; 1400°R; q)$; $(A; 3300°R; 720)$;
$(18.5; T; 400)$

Example: $q = 0.174 \times 5.2 \left(\dfrac{1800}{100}\right)^4 = 94{,}000$

The LogLog scales are less accurate for finding 18^4 than the simple power scales, and the answer must be factored into $18^2 \times 18^2$, for example, in using some LogLog scales.

PROBLEM 7.2I. *Fluid Mechanics.* Theoretical Venturi flow rate is given by

$$Q = \frac{A_2}{\sqrt{1 - \left(\dfrac{A_2}{A_1}\right)^2}} \sqrt{\frac{2g}{w}(P_1 - P_2)} \qquad \text{(cu ft per sec)}$$

where A_1 and A_2 are areas in sq ft, P_1 and P_2 are pressures in lb per sq ft, g is acceleration of gravity in ft per sec², w is specific weight of fluid in lb per cu ft.

Data: $(A_1; A_2; P_1; P_2; w; Q)$; $(1.00; 0.52; 11.6; 4.9; 62.4; Q)$; $(0.82; 0.36; P_1; 21; 56; 4.7)$; $(0.17; 0.051; 34.0; 3.8; w; 0.43)$; $(A_1; 0.25; 77; 17; 0.076; 71)$

Example: $Q = \dfrac{0.52}{\sqrt{1 - 0.52^2}} \sqrt{\dfrac{2 \times 32.2}{62.4}(11.6 - 4.9)}$

$\qquad = 0.52 \sqrt{\dfrac{64.4 \times 6.7}{62.4 \times 0.73}} = 1.60$

PROBLEM 7.2J. *Machine Design.* The load which may safely be placed on a coil spring is given by

$$F = \frac{\pi d^3 S}{8DK} \qquad \text{(lbs)}$$

where d is wire diam, in., S is allowable shear stress, lb per sq in., D is coil diam, in., K is Wall's Factor.

Data: $S = 55{,}000$; $K = 1.25$; $(d; D; F)$; $(0.375; 2.5; F)$; $(d; 4.5; 1750)$; $(0.460; D; 1180)$; $(0.125; 0.83; F)$

Example: $F = \dfrac{\pi \times 0.375^3 \times 55{,}000}{8 \times 2.5 \times 1.25} = 364$

Mentally, $8 \times 1.25 = 10$, and $10 \times 2.5 = 25$. The 0.375^3 may be read as 0.0528 and $\pi \times 55{,}000 \times 0.0528/25 = 364$.

PROBLEM 7.2K. *Machine Design.* The deflection of a coil spring is given by

$$y = \frac{8FD^3 n}{d^4 G} \qquad \text{(in.)}$$

where F is load in lbs, D is coil diam in., n is number of active coils, d is wire diam in., and G is shear modulus in lbs per sq in. If the values of n

for the springs of Problem 7.2J are 9, 17, 27, and 13 respectively, find the deflections for $G = 12{,}000{,}000$.

Example: $y = \dfrac{8 \times 972 \times 2.5^3 \times 9}{0.375^4 \times 12 \times 10^6} = 4.61$

Obtain 2.5^3 and 0.375^4 separately, then since $8 \times 9/12 = 6$, this reduces to

$$y = \frac{6 \times 972 \times 15.6}{0.01975 \times 10^6}$$

PROBLEM 7.2L. *Machine Design.* The relationship between diameters of hollow and solid shafts having the same maximum stress is

$$D_0^3 = \frac{D^3}{1 - K^4}$$

where D_0 is outside diam of hollow shaft, D is diam of solid shaft, and K is the ratio of inside diam, D_i, to outside diam for the hollow shaft.

Data: $(D; K; D_0; D_i)$; $(3.5; 0.5; D_0; D_i)$; $(D; K; 4.0; 3.0)$; $(1.6; K; 2.0; D_i)$; $(3.25; 0.875; D_0; D_i)$

Example: The arithmetic may be shortened by writing

$$D_0 = \frac{3.5}{\sqrt[3]{1 - 0.5^4}} = 3.58; \; D_i = 0.5 \times 3.58 = 1.79$$

PROBLEM 7.2M. *Fluid Mechanics.* The rate of flow of water over a triangular notch weir is given by

$$Q = 0.305 H^{5/2} \tan \frac{\theta}{2} \qquad \text{(cu ft per min)}$$

where H is the head in in., θ is angle of notch.

Data: $(H; \theta; Q)$; $(2.5; 90°; Q)$; $(8.5; \theta; 66)$; $(4.7; 80°; Q)$; $(H; 100°; 44)$

Example: $Q = 0.305 \times 2.5^{5/2} = 3.02$

The 5/2 power may be obtained with LogLog scales, or this example may be written

$$2.5^{5/2} = 2.5 \times 2.5^{3/2}$$

and solved as shown in Chapter 2.

PROBLEM 7.2N. *Fluid Mechanics.* The Manning formula for steady uniform flow of a liquid is

$$V = \frac{1.49}{n} R^{2/3} S^{1/2}$$

where n is roughness factor in ft, R is hydraulic depth in ft, S is the slope of energy grade line, V is speed in ft per sec.

Data: $(n; R; S; V)$; $(0.016; 0.27; 0.52; V)$; $(0.030; 0.40; S; 0.56)$; $(0.022;$
$R; 0.30; 1.10)$; $(n; 0.16; 0.75; 7.2)$

Example: $V = \dfrac{1.49}{0.016} \, 0.27^{2/3} \, 0.52^{1/2} = 28.1$

PROBLEM 7.2P. *Electrical Engineering.* The energy stored in a magnetic field under steady current conditions is given by

$$W = \frac{LI^2}{2} \qquad \text{(watts)}$$

where L is inductance in henrys and I is current in amps.

Data: $(L; I; W)$; $(0.42; 75; W)$; $(1.7; I; 450)$; $(L; 27; 840)$; $(0.37; 18.5; W)$

Example: $W = \dfrac{0.42 \times 75^2}{2} = 1180$

PROBLEM 7.2Q. *Thermodynamics.* Van der Waal's Equation

$$\left(P + \frac{a}{v^2}\right)(v - b) = RT$$

if solved for v leads to a cubic equation. For nitrogen the constants a, b, and R are 344, 0.617, and 0.729 respectively, where P is pressure in atmospheres and T is temperature in degrees Rankine.

Data: $(P; T; v)$; $(100; 1000°R; v)$; $(500; T; 1.8)$; $(200; 1200°R; v)$; $(350;$
$960°R; v)$

Example: $\left(100 + \dfrac{344}{v^2}\right)(v - 0.617) = 0.729 \times 1000$

or

$$v^2 + 3.44 = 7.907v + \frac{2.12}{v}$$

Several trials, such as $v = 1$, $v = 7$, $v = 7.5$, lead to $v = 7.48$ as one solution.

7.3. Trigonometric Calculations.

PROBLEM 7.3A. *Structures.* In the design of roof trusses the Duchemin formula for wind loads is often used, Fig. 7.2.

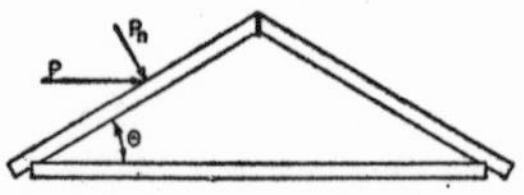

Fig. 7.2. Roof Wind Load

$$P_n = P \frac{2 \sin \theta}{1 + \sin^2 \theta}$$

where P is horizontal wind pressure in lb per sq ft, θ is roof angle with horizontal, P_n is pressure normal to roof.

Data: $(\theta; \tan \theta; P; P_n)$; $(10°; \tan \theta; 22; P_n)$; $(\theta; 1/6; 27; P_n)$; $(\theta; 1/4; 30;$
$P_n)$; $(20°; \tan \theta; 26; P_n)$

Example: $P_n = \dfrac{22 \times 2 \sin 10°}{1 + \sin^2 10°} = \dfrac{44 \times 0.1736}{1 + 0.1736^2} = 7.40;\ \tan \theta = 0.176$

PROBLEM 7.3B. *Machine Design.* The velocity ratio for helical gears is given by

$$\frac{w_1}{w_2} = \frac{D_2 \cos \phi_2}{D_1 \cos \phi_1}$$

where subscripts 1 and 2 refer to gears 1 and 2, ϕ's are corresponding helix angles, D's are pitch diam.

Data: $(D_1;\ D_2;\ \phi_1;\ \phi_2;\ w_1/w_2);$ $(8'';\ 12'';\ 14°30';\ 30°30';\ w_1/w_2);$ $(7.5'';\ D_2;\ 18°;\ 41°;\ 1.95);$ $(5'';\ 16'';\ 20°;\ \phi_2;\ 2.8);$ $(9'';\ 8.5'';\ \phi_1;\ 23°30';\ 0.92)$

Example: $\dfrac{w_1}{w_2} = \dfrac{12 \cos 30°30'}{8 \cos 14°30'} = 1.34$

PROBLEM 7.3C. *Machine Design.* The efficiency of a screw is given by

$$E = \frac{\tan \alpha}{\tan (\alpha + \phi)}$$

where α is the helix angle, and $\tan \phi$ equals the coefficient of friction.

Data: $(\alpha;\ \phi;\ \tan \phi;\ E);$ $(1.5°;\ \phi;\ 0.12;\ E);$ $(2.5°;\ 7.5°;\ \tan \phi;\ E);$ $(2°15';\ \phi;\ \tan \phi;\ 0.22);$ $(2.3°;\ \phi;\ 0.082;\ E)$

Example: Set hairline to 0.12 on C
       Read $\phi = 6.9°$ on T
       Then $\alpha + \phi = 8.4°$
       Align indices and set hairline to 1.5° on ST
       Place 8.4° on T beneath hairline
       Read $E = 0.177$ on D at index of C

PROBLEM 7.3D. *Mechanics.* The angle at which maximum shear occurs in combined shear and tension is given by

$$\theta_s = \frac{1}{2} \tan^{-1} \frac{S_t}{2S_s}$$

where S_t is tension stress and S_s is shear stress in the same units.

Data: $(S_s;\ S_t;\ \theta_s;\ \tan 2\theta_s);$ $(16{,}000;\ 37{,}000;\ \theta_s;\ \tan 2\theta_s);$ $(1700;\ S_t;\ 17.5°;\ \tan 2\theta_s);$ $(S_s;\ 2300;\ \theta_s;\ 0.97);$ $(4200;\ 1200;\ \theta_s;\ \tan 2\theta_s)$

Example: $\tan 2\theta_s = 37{,}000/(2 \times 16{,}000) = 1.156$
       $\theta_s = 49.2°/2 = 24.6°$

PROBLEM 7.3E. *Mechanics.* The acceleration of the crosshead on a steam engine is given approximately by

$$a = rw^2 \left(\cos \theta + \frac{r}{l} \cos 2\theta \right)$$

where r is radius of crank arm in ft, w is angular velocity of the crank in radians per sec, θ is crank arm position, l is length of connecting rod in ft, a is then in ft per sec^2

Data: $(r; w; \theta; l; a)$; $(0.83; 4.5; 45°; 2.75; a)$; $(0.83; 4.5; 105°; 2.75; a)$; $(1.25; w; 70°; 3.50; 1.85)$; $(0.67; w; 60°; 2.50; 3.50)$

Example: $a = 0.83 \times 4.5^2 \left(\cos 45° + \frac{r}{l} \cos 90° \right)$

$= 0.83 \times 4.5^2 \times 0.707 = 11.9$

PROBLEM 7.3F. *Electric Power.* In single phase electrical circuits the power is given by

$$P = EI \cos \theta$$

where P is power in watts, E is effective volts across circuit, I is current through circuit in amperes, and $\cos \theta$ is power factor, or θ is power factor angle.

Data: $(E; I; \theta; \cos \theta; P)$; $(240; 18.2; 20°; \cos \theta; P)$; $(E; 37.0; \theta; 0.78; 3320)$; $(E; 21.9; 33°; \cos \theta; 8100)$; $(550; 1.77; \theta; 0.89; P)$

Example: $P = 240 \times 18.2 \times \cos 20° = 4100$

PROBLEM 7.3G. *Electric Power.* In balanced three phase electrical circuits the power is given by

$$P = \sqrt{3} \, EI \cos \theta$$

where E is line-to-line effective volts and I is current in each line, $\cos \theta$ again is power factor.

Data: $(E; I; \theta; \cos \theta; P)$; $(13{,}200; 52.0; 15°; \cos \theta; P)$; $(3900; I; \theta; 0.92; 61{,}000)$; $(E; 17.9; 29°; \cos \theta; 58{,}000)$; $(132{,}000; 68.5; \theta; 0.88; P)$

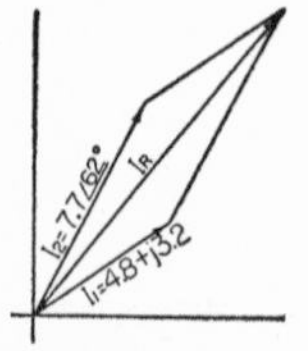

Example: $P = \sqrt{3} \times 13{,}200 \times 52.0 \times \cos 15° = 114{,}800$

Fig. 7.3. Composition of Electric Current Vectors

PROBLEM 7.3H. *Electrical Circuits.* The effective values of alternating currents are often represented as vectors related to a rectangular coordinate system, Fig. 7.3, and expressed either as I/θ or as $I_x + jI_y$. The vector sum of several such currents is obtained by expressing all in terms of components along the axes and adding.

Data: $(I_1; I_2; I)$; $(4.8 + j3.2; 7.7\underline{/62°}; I)$; $(57.5\overline{/27°}; 15.2 + j11.5; I)$; $(3.5\overline{/45°}; I_2; 75\overline{/86°})$; $(I_1; 0.0037 - j0.09; 0.15\underline{/31°})$

Example: $I_2 = 7.7\underline{/62°} = 3.61 + j6.8$
$I_1 = 4.8 + j3.2$
$I = 8.41 + j10.0 = 13.05\underline{/50.0°}$

PROBLEM 7.3I. *Electrical Circuits.* The equivalent impedance for several impedances in parallel requires addition of their admittances (or reciprocals) expressed in complex notation form.

$$\frac{1}{Z} = \frac{1}{Z_1} + \frac{1}{Z_2} + \frac{1}{Z_3} + \cdots$$

Three impedances only are present in the problems appearing here.

Data: $(Z_1; Z_2; Z_3; Z)$; $(17.7\underline{/45°}; 8.3\underline{/16°}; 6.5\underline{/0°}; Z)$; $(3.76\underline{/18°}; 12.8\underline{/27°}; Z_3; 2.95\underline{/25°})$; $(58.5\overline{/72°}; 23.0\overline{/10°}; 13\overline{/20°}; Z)$; $(11.7\overline{/38°}; 4.7\underline{/57°}; 9.3\underline{/62°}; Z)$

Example: $1/Z_1 = 1/17.7$ at $\underline{/45°} = 0.0565\underline{/45°}$
$= 0.0399 - j0.0399$
$1/Z_2 = 0.1205\underline{/16°} = 0.116 + j0.0332$
$1/Z_3 = 0.154 + j0$
$1/Z = 0.3099 - j0.0067 = 0.310\overline{/1.24°}$
$Z = 3.23\underline{/1.24°}$

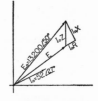

F i g . 7 . 4 .
Voltage Drop
Vector Diagram

PROBLEM 7.3J. *Electrical Engineering.* The voltage relations in an alternating current circuit may be similar to the vector diagram of Fig. 7.4, or

$$E = E_0 - I_0 Z$$

Data: $E_0 = 13,200\underline{/50°}$; $I_0 = 52\underline{/27°}$; (Z); $(17 + j34; 48\overline{/22°}; 21 - j16; 35\underline{/61°})$

Example: $Z = 17 + j34 = 38.0\underline{/63.45°}$; $E_0 = 10,100 + j8480$

$I_0 Z = 52\underline{/27°} \times 38.0\underline{/63.45°} = 1975\underline{/90.45°}$

$= -\dfrac{0.45 \times 1975}{57.3} + j1975 = -15.5 + j1975$

$E = 10,100 + j8480 - (15.5 + j1975)$

$= 10,085 + j6505$, or $11,900\underline{/33°}$

PROBLEM 7.3K. *Structural Design.* The secant formula for maximum deflection in a column under eccentric loading is

$$Y_m = e \sec \frac{l}{2} \sqrt{\frac{P}{EI}} \qquad \text{(in.)}$$

where e is eccentricity in in., l is column length in in., P is load in lb, E is modulus of elasticity in lb per sq in., I is moment of inertia in in.^{4}; the angle then is in radians.

Data: $E = 29 \times 10^6$; $(P; I; l; e; Y_m)$; $(27{,}000; 18.6; 120''; 0.7; Y_m)$; $(48{,}000; 24.8; 180''; e; 1.48)$; $(P; 10.5; 144''; 0.9; 1.3)$; $(85{,}000; 36.7; l; 1.2; 1.7)$

Example: $Y_m = 0.7 \times \sec \dfrac{120}{2} \sqrt{\dfrac{27 \times 10^3}{29 \times 10^6 \times 18.6}}$

$= 0.7 \sec 0.424$

or

$$= \frac{0.7}{\cos 24.3°} = 0.77$$

Standard numbers are helpful for placing the decimal point in the quantity under the radical. It reduces to 5×10^{-5}, or 50×10^{-6}. The angle in radians must be converted to degrees for slide rule operation, and 0.424 radians $= 24.3°$.

PROBLEM 7.3L. *Structural Design.* The ultimate strength of an eccentrically loaded column is given by

$$S = \frac{P}{A}\left(1 + \frac{ec}{r^2} \sec \frac{l}{2r} \sqrt{\frac{P}{AE}}\right) \qquad \text{(lb per sq in.)}$$

where P is load lb, A is area of column sq in., e is eccentricity in in., c is distance from center of gravity to extreme fiber in in., r is radius of gyration about axis of bending in in., E is modulus of elasticity in lb per sq in., l is length of column in in., S is elastic limit strength of column material.

Data: $E = 29 \times 10^6$; $(P; e; l; A; r; c; S)$; $(90{,}000; 1.25; 120; 9.71; 1.94; 4.88; S)$; $(P; 0.75; 180; 11.77; 1.94; 5.97; 15{,}000)$; $(145{,}000; 1.75; 192; 19.11; 3.02; 6.06; S)$; $(23{,}000; 0.50; 168; 4.62; 1.45; 3.00; S)$

The first set of data reduces to

$$S = 9280(1 + 1.62 \sec 0.553)$$

or on converting radians to degrees

$$S = 9280\left(1 + \frac{1.62}{\cos 31.6°}\right) = 26{,}900$$

PROBLEM 7.3M. *Machine Design.* The moment transmitted by a worm gear is given by

$$M_t = W\left(r_m \frac{\tan \alpha + f/\cos \theta}{1 - f \tan \alpha/\cos \theta} + f_c r_c\right) \qquad \text{(in.-lb)}$$

where W is load in lb, r_m is the radius of the screw thread in in., θ is the angle between the thread face and plane perpendicular to axis, α is helix angle, r_c is radius of bearing collar in in., f is thread coefficient of friction, f_c is bearing collar coefficient of friction.

Data: $\theta = 14\ 1/2°$; $f = 0.015$; $f_c = 0.010$; $(r_m;\ W;\ \alpha;\ \tan \alpha;\ r_c;\ M_t)$; $(2/3;\ 500;\ \alpha;\ 1/4\pi;\ 1.75;\ M_t)$; $(0.50;\ W;\ 4°35';\ \tan \alpha;\ 1.25;\ 96)$; $(1.25;\ 1100;\ \alpha;\ 1/5\pi;\ 2.50;\ M_t)$; $(1.25;\ W;\ 6°20';\ \tan \alpha;\ 3.00;\ 200)$

Example: $M_t = 500\left(\dfrac{2}{3}\dfrac{1/4\pi + 0.015/\cos 14.5°}{1 - 0.015/4\pi \cos 14.5°} + 0.010 \times 1.75\right)$
$= 40.5$

7.4. Logarithmic and Exponential Calculations. PROBLEM 7.4A. *Thermodynamics.* The work done in an isothermal process is given by

$$W_K = 144 P_1 V_1 \ln \frac{V_2}{V_1} \quad \text{(ft-lb)}$$

where P_1 is in lb per sq in., V_1 and V_2 are in cu ft.

Data: $(P_1;\ V_1;\ V_2;\ W_K)$; $(125;\ 3.7;\ 19.5;\ W_K)$; $(P_1;\ 4.8;\ 13.5;\ 8000)$; $(250;\ 2.5;\ V_2;\ 9000)$; $(520;\ 4.2;\ 15.5;\ W_K)$

Example: $W_K'' = 144 \times 127 \times 3.7 \ln \dfrac{19.5}{3.7} = 11.25^{+4}$

$\dfrac{19.5}{3.7} = 5.27$; $\ln 5.27 = 1.66$

The product of four numbers is obtained faster by using inverted scales along with direct, and in this example folded scales also mean less movement of the slide.

Set hairline to 1.66 on DF
Move slide to place 127 on CIF beneath hairline
Set hairline to 3.7 on C
Place 144 on CI beneath hairline
Read 11.25 on D at index of CI

PROBLEM 7.4B. *Thermodynamics.* For a polytropic process the relationship between pressures and volumes is

$$\frac{P_1}{P_2} = \left(\frac{V_2}{V_1}\right)^n$$

where P_1, P_2, are initial and final pressures and V_1, V_2, are initial and final volumes.

Data: $(P_1;\ P_2;\ V_1;\ V_2;\ n)$; $(75;\ 900;\ 6;\ V_2;\ 1.41)$; $(P_1;\ 650;\ 14;\ 140;\ 1.41)$; $(850;\ 240;\ 1.70;\ 4.50;\ n)$; $(675;\ 125;\ V_1;\ 4.50;\ 1.31)$

Example: $\dfrac{75}{900} = \left(\dfrac{V_2}{6}\right)^{1.41}$ or $V_2 = 6\left(\dfrac{75}{900}\right)^{1/1.41}$

$V_2 = 6(0.0833)^{0.709} = 6 \times 0.172 = 1.03$

PROBLEM 7.4C. *Machine Design.* An empirical equation giving the permissible power transmitted by a worm gear is

$$hp = \frac{9.5C^{1.7}}{(R + 5)} \qquad \text{(horsepower)}$$

where C is center distance from axis of worm to axis of gear in in., R is velocity ratio of worm and gear.

Data: $(C; R; hp); (7; 12; hp); (C; 10; 30); (15; 18; hp); (C; 8; 10)$

Example: $hp = 9.5 \times 7^{1.7}/17 = 9.5 \times 27.5/17 = 15.3$

PROBLEM 7.4D. *Heat Transfer.* Heat conduction through cylindrical surfaces is given by

$$q' = \frac{2\pi k(T_1 - T_2)}{\ln \dfrac{D_2}{D_1}} \qquad \text{(Btu per hr per ft)}$$

where D_1 and D_2 are inner and outer diameters of the shell, T_1 and T_2 are inner and outer temperatures of the shell in degrees F, k is conductance of the material in $(\text{Btu-hr-degree-ft})^{-1}$.

Data: $(k; T_1; T_2; D_1; D_2; q'); (0.0375; 380°; 80°; 2''; 4''; q'); (1.5; T_1; 80°; 4''; 7''; 100); (0.022; 360°; 70°; 4''; D_2; 250); (35.0; 400°; T_2; 3''; 5''; 185)$

Example: $q' = \dfrac{2\pi \times 0.0375 \times 300}{\ln 2} = \dfrac{2\pi \times 0.0375 \times 300}{0.693} = 102$

PROBLEM 7.4E. *Heat Transfer.* The relationship between Nusselt's number, Reynolds' number and Prandtl's number is given by

$$(Nu) = 0.33(Re)^{0.6}(Pr)^{1/3}$$

Data: $(Nu; Re; Pr); (Nu; 8000; 6.3); (1340; 10{,}600; Pr); (1100; Re; 3.5); (5100; Re; 1.5)$

Example: $(Nu) = 0.33(8000)^{0.6}(6.3)^{1/3}$
$= 0.33 \times 220 \times 1.85 = 134$

PROBLEM 7.4F. *Electrical Transmission.* The inductive reactance to neutral for a three-phase open wire line is given by

$$X = 2\pi f S \left(0.322 \ln \frac{D}{r} + 0.0805\right) \times 10^{-3}$$

At $f = 60$ cycles per sec this reduces to

$$X = \left(0.1213 \ln \frac{D}{r} + 0.0303\right) S \quad \text{(ohms)}$$

where D is equivalent spacing of conductors, r is radius of conductor, S is length of line in miles.

Data: $(D; r; S; X)$; $(120; 0.230; 45; X)$; $(180; 0.576; S; 52)$; $(D; 0.706; 36.3; 37.5)$; $(210; r; 25.0; 19.1)$

Example: $X = \left(0.1213 \ln \dfrac{120}{0.23} + 0.0303\right) 45$

$= (0.76 + 0.0303)45 = 35.6$

PROBLEM 7.4G. *Heat Transfer.* The logarithmic mean temperature difference is given by

$$\Delta T = \frac{T_1 - T_2}{\ln \dfrac{T_1}{T_2}}$$

where T_1 and T_2 are absolute temperatures, to any scale. Find ΔT for the following pairs of temperatures: $(920°\text{R}; 650°\text{R})$; $(1800°\text{R}; 1400°\text{R})$; $(500°\text{R}; 420°\text{R})$; $(1250°\text{R}; 740°\text{R})$.

Example: $\Delta T = \dfrac{920 - 650}{\ln \dfrac{920}{650}} = \dfrac{270}{\ln 1.416} = \dfrac{270}{0.348} = 777$

Solution for ΔT is straight forward, although subtraction, division, log to base e, and another division are required. If ΔT and T_2 are given, T_1 can be found, but only by trial, or by plotting a graph of ΔT versus T_1 and reading from the graph.

PROBLEM 7.4H. *Thermodynamics.* The polytropic work of expansion is given by

$$W = \frac{144 P_1 V_1}{1 - n}\left[\left(\frac{V_2}{V_1}\right)^{1-n} - 1\right] \quad \text{(ft-lb)}$$

where V_1, V_2, are initial and final volumes in cu ft, P_1 is initial pressure in lb per sq in.

Data: $(P_1; V_1; V_2; n; W)$; $(290; 4.0; 15.5; 1.26; W)$; $(P_1; 3.5; 18.0; 1.21; 160,000)$; $(160; 6.2; V_2; 1.30; 125,000)$; $(210, 5.5; 21.0; 1.30; W)$

Example: $W = \dfrac{144 \times 290 \times 4}{1 - 1.26}\left[\left(\dfrac{15.5}{4.0}\right)^{1-1.26} - 1\right]$

$= \dfrac{144 \times 290 \times 4}{0.26}\left[1 - \left(\dfrac{4.0}{15.5}\right)^{0.26}\right]$

and

$$\left(\frac{4.0}{15.5}\right)^{0.26} = 0.258^{0.26} = 0.704$$

$$W = \frac{144 \times 290 \times 0.296 \times 4}{0.26} = 190,000 \text{ ft-lb}$$

PROBLEM 7.4I. *Electrical Engineering.* The transient current on closing a circuit containing inductance and resistance is given by

$$I = \frac{E}{R}(1 - e^{-Rt/L})$$

where E is potential in volts, R is resistance in ohms, L is inductance in henrys, t is time in seconds.

Data: $(E; R; L; t; I)$; $(120; 16; 0.07; 0.004; I)$; $(440; 75; 0.40; t; 3.7)$; $(375; 40; L; 0.010; 4.2)$; $(E; 1.27; 0.014; 0.006; 2.2)$

Example: $I = \dfrac{120}{16}\left(1 - e^{\frac{-16 \times 0.004}{0.07}}\right)$

$$= 7.50(1 - e^{-0.914}) = 7.50(1 - 0.40) = 4.50$$

PROBLEM 7.4J. *Electrical Engineering.* The maximum electrical gradient in an insulated cable is given by

$$E_G = \frac{E}{r \ln \dfrac{R}{r}}$$

where E is maximum potential between sheath and conductor, R is inside radius of sheath, r is radius of conductor.

Data: $(E; R; r; E_G)$; $(45,000; 2.3; 0.23; E_G)$; $(E; 1.6; 0.38; 75,000)$; $(66,000; R; 0.86; 95,000)$; $(18,700; 2.0; r; 40,000)$

Example: $E_G = \dfrac{45,000}{0.23 \ln \dfrac{2.3}{0.23}} = \dfrac{45,000}{0.23 \ln 10} = \dfrac{45,000}{0.23 \times 2.30}$

If r is to be found, as in the last set of data, a trial procedure is required.

PROBLEM 7.4K. *Fluid Mechanics.* For turbulent flow Reynolds number, N_R, and friction factor, f, are related by

$$\frac{1}{\sqrt{f}} = 2 \log N_R \sqrt{f} - 0.8$$

Data: $f = 0.04; 0.06; 0.08; N_R = 50,000$

$$\frac{1}{\sqrt{0.04}} = 2 \log \sqrt{0.04}\, N_R - 0.8$$

This reduces to

$$\log 0.2 N_R = 2.900; \text{ or, } N_R = 3970$$

If N_R is given, as in the last item of data, a trial solution or a graph is needed to find f.

PROBLEM 7.4L. *Fluid Mechanics, Thermodynamics.* The critical gas pressure in a nozzle is given by

$$P_x = P\left(\frac{2}{k+1}\right)^{\frac{k}{k-1}}$$

where P is nozzle entrance pressure and k is a function of the gas used.

Data: $(P; \text{Gas}; k; P_x)$; $(150; \text{Air}; 1.41; P_x)$; $(220; \text{Argon}; 1.66; P_x)$; $(P; \text{Air}; 1.41; 116)$; $(P; CO_2; 1.32 \text{ av.}; 60)$

Example: $P_x = 150\left(\dfrac{2}{1.41+1}\right)^{\frac{1.41}{0.41}}$; $150(0.83)^{3.44} = 79.0$

PROBLEM 7.4M. *Thermodynamics.* The thermal efficiency of the Otto cycle is given by

$$n = 1 - \frac{1}{r^{k-1}}$$

where r is compression ratio and k is 1.41.

Data: $(r; n)$; $(5.1; n)$; $(8.7; n)$; $(r; 0.62)$; $(r; 0.71)$

Example: $n = 1 - 1/5.1^{0.41} = 0.487$

PROBLEM 7.4N. *Thermodynamics.* The thermal efficiency of the diesel cycle is given by

$$n = 1 - \frac{1}{k}\left(\frac{1}{r}\right)^{k-1}\left[\frac{1 - r_c^{k}}{1 - r_c}\right]$$

where k is 1.41, r is compression ratio, r_c is cut-off ratio.

Data: $(r; r_c; n)$; $(8.0; 0.059; n)$; $(r; 0.04; 0.55)$; $(10.0; 0.072; n)$; $(r; 0.06; 0.62)$

Example: $n = 1 - \dfrac{0.125^{0.41}}{1.41}\left(\dfrac{1 - 0.059^{1.41}}{1 - 0.059}\right)$

$\qquad = 1 - \dfrac{0.426}{1.41}\left(\dfrac{1 - 0.0184}{0.941}\right) = 0.684$

PROBLEM 7.4P. *Fluid Mechanics.* Pressures for a fluid flowing in a pipe are related by

$$P_2{}^2 - P_1{}^2 = \frac{V_1{}^2 P_1}{g v_1}\left[2\ln\frac{V_2}{V_1} + \frac{fl}{D}\right]$$

where P_1 and P_2 are exit and entrance pressures in lb per sq ft, V_1 and V_2 are exit and entrance average velocities in ft per sec, v_1 is specific volume in cu ft per lb, f is friction coefficient, l and D are length and diameter of pipe in ft.

Data: $v_1 = 3.33$; $f = 0.012$; $g = 32.2$ ft/sec^2; $(l; D; V_1; V_2; P_1; P_2)$; $(5000; 0.5; 18; 16; 9000; P_2)$; $(4000; 1.0; 25; 23; 11,000; P_2)$; $(8000; 0.75; 32; 30; 15,000)$

Example: $P_2{}^2 = 9000^2 + \dfrac{18^2 \times 9000}{32.2 \times 3.33}\left(2 \ln \dfrac{16}{18} + \dfrac{0.012 \times 5000}{0.5}\right)$

$\qquad = 81 \times 10^6 + 27{,}200(-0.236 + 120)$

$\qquad P_2 = 9180$

PROBLEM 7.4Q. *Electrical Engineering.* For electrically long transmission lines

$$E_S = E_R \cosh \sqrt{ZY} + I_R \sqrt{Z/Y} \sinh \sqrt{ZY}$$

where E_S and E_R are sending and receiving end voltages, I_R is receiving end current, Z is series impedance of line, and Y is shunt admittance of line.

Z	Y	E_R	E_S	I_R
$40 + j250$	$j0.0016$	$300{,}000 + j0$		$200 - j100$
$40 + j250$	$0.0004 + j0.0016$		$300{,}000 + j0$	$300 - j150$
$80 + j500$	$j0.0008$	$300{,}000 + j0$		$200 - j100$

Example: The solution of this problem with its complex hyperbolic functions requires more slide rule manipulation than appears at first glance. The procedure is indicated in some detail.

$$ZY = j0.0016(40 + j250) = -0.40 + j0.064 = 0.405\underline{/170.9°}$$

$$\sqrt{ZY} = \sqrt{0.405}\ \underline{/170.9°}/2 = 0.636\underline{/85.45°} = 0.0505 + j0.616$$

$$\frac{Z}{Y} = \frac{253.2\underline{/80.9°}}{0.0016\underline{/90°}} = 158{,}000\underline{/9.1°}$$

$$\sqrt{Z/Y} = 398\underline{/4.55°}$$

$$E_S = 300{,}000\underline{/0°} \times \cosh 0.636\underline{/85.45°}$$
$$\qquad\qquad + 224\underline{/26.5°} \times 398\underline{/4.55°} \times \sinh 0.636\underline{/85.45°}$$

The hyperbolic functions of complex angles may be reduced by the following identities.

$$\cosh(a + jb) = \cosh a \cos b + j \sinh a \sin b$$
$$\sinh(a + jb) = \sinh a \cos b + j \cosh a \sin b$$

thence

$$\cosh (0.0505 + j0.616) = \cosh 0.0505 \cos 0.616 + j \sinh 0.0505 \sin 0.616$$

and

$$\cosh 0.0505 = \frac{e^{0.0505} + e^{-0.0505}}{2} = \frac{1.0518 + 0.9510}{2}$$

$$\sinh 0.0505 = \frac{(1.0518 - 0.9510)}{2}$$

$$0.616 \text{ radians} = 35.4°$$

The number e raised to both positive and negative powers can be read in one setting from slide rules on which all LogLog scales are associated with the D scale. For example, using the slide rule of Fig. A.3

Set hairline to 0.0505 on D
Read $e^{0.0505}$ on LL1
Read $e^{-0.0505}$ on LL01

$$\cosh 0.636\underline{/85.45°} = 0.865\underline{/18.4°}; \sinh 0.636\underline{/85.45°} = 0.581\underline{/86.2°}$$

Now

$$E_s = 300,000\underline{/0°} \times 0.865\underline{/18.4°} + 51,900\underline{/54.4°}$$
$$= (246,000 + j81,900) + (30,200 + j42,200)$$
$$= 303,000\underline{/24.2°}$$

PROBLEM 7.4R. *Electrical Engineering.* The currents in electrically long transmission lines such as those of Problem 7.4Q are related by

$$I_S = I_R \cosh \sqrt{ZY} + \left(\frac{E_R}{\sqrt{Z/Y}}\right) \sinh \sqrt{ZY}$$

For the example in the preceding problem

$$I_S = 253.2\underline{/80.9°} \times 0.865\underline{/18.4°} + \frac{300,000\underline{/0°} \times 0.581\underline{/86.2°}}{398\underline{/4.55°}}$$
$$= 218.5\underline{/99.3°} + 438\underline{/90.75°}$$
$$= (-35.3 + j215.7) + (-5.7 + j438) = 654\underline{/93.6°}$$

In a similar way I_S may be calculated for the other sets of data in the preceding problem.

PROBLEM 7.4S. *Mechanics.* The long uniform suspended cable hangs in a catenary expressed by

$$y = C\left(\cosh \frac{S}{2C} - 1\right)$$
$$L = 2C \sinh \frac{S}{2C}$$

where S is span, y is sag, L is length, and C is a constant, all being in the same units.

Data: $(S; C; y; L)$; $(2000; 2000; y; L)$; $(2000; C; 400; L)$; $(4000; 3000;$ $y; L)$

Example: $y = 2000(\cosh 0.5 - 1)$

$$= 2000 \left(\frac{1.648 + 0.606}{2} - 1 \right) = 254$$

$$L = 4000 \sinh 0.5 = 4000 \times 0.521 = 2084$$

If S and L, or S and y, are given, as is often the case in practical problems, a succession of trials or plotting a graph is necessary to obtain the other quantities.

So-called "Vector" slide rules on which the sinh or tanh can be read directly without addition or subtraction of terms are helpful on problems such as these last three.

APPENDICES

A.1. DATA ON SELECTED COMMERCIAL SLIDE RULES

	A.1	A.2	A.3	A.4	A.5	A.6	A.7	A.8
Fig. No.	A.1	A.2	A.3	A.4	A.5	A.6	A.7	A.8
Trade Name	Maniphase Mannheim	Polyphase Duplex	LogLog Duplex Decitrig	Maniphase Multiplex Decimal Trig	Deci-LogLog Model No. 2	800	Versalog	LogLog Trig
Manufacturer	Dietzgen	Keuffel & Esser	Keuffel & Esser	Dietzgen	Pickett & Eckel	Pickett & Eckel	Frederick Post Co.	Keuffel & Esser
Cat. No.	1761	4088-3	N4081-3	1732	2	800		4090-3
Form	Mannheim	—	Duplex	Duplex	Duplex	Duplex	Duplex	Duplex
Type			Log Log	Log Log	Log Log	Log Log	Log Log	Log Log
Scale Position — Top of Frame	F: A	F: DF; B: K	F: LL02, LL03, DF; B: LL01, K, A	F: LL02, LL03, DF; B: LL01, K, A	F: $\sqrt[3]{\ }$, $\sqrt[3]{\ }$, $\sqrt[3]{\ }$, DF; B: $N_1,1/N_1$, $N_2,1/N_2$, DF/M	F: LL2, DF; B: LL1, A	F: LL0, LL/0, K, DF; B: LL/1, LL/2, LL/3	F: L, LL1, DF; B: LL0, A
Scale Position — Slide	F: B, CI, C; B: S, L, T	F: CF, CIF, C; B: A, B, S, T, CI	F: CF, CIF, CI, C; B: B, T, ST, S	F: CF, CIF, CI, C; B: B, T, ST, S	F: CF, T, ST, S, CI, C; B: CF/M, L, CI, C	F: CF, CIF, L, CI, C; B: B, ST, T, S, C	F: CF, CIF, CI, C; B: T, ST, S, C	F: CF, CIF, C; B: B, K, CI
Scale Position — Bottom of Frame	F: D	F: D; B: D, L	F: D, LL3, LL2; B: D, L, LL1	F: D, LL3, LL2; B: D, L, LL1	F: D, DI, $\sqrt{\ }$; B: D, $N_3,1/N_3$, $N_4,1/N_4$	F: LL3; B: DI, D, K	F: D, R_1, R_2, L; B: D, LL3, LL2, LL1	F: D, LL3, LL2; B: T, S2, S1

(F = Front, B = Back)

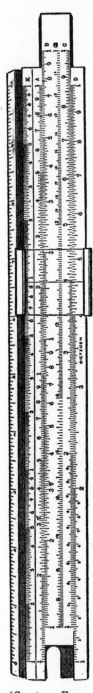

(Courtesy, Eugene Dietzgen Co.)
Fig. A.1. Maniphase Mannheim (Eugene
Dietzgen Co., trademark)

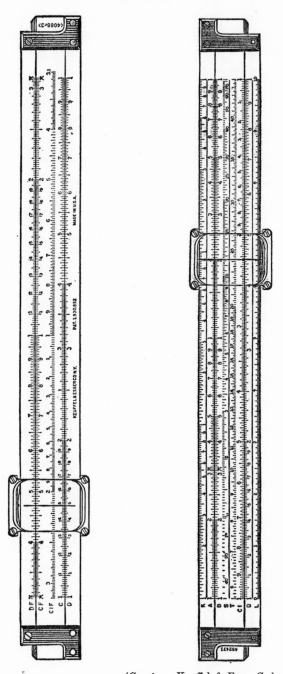

(Courtesy, Keuffel & Esser Co.)

(front) (back)

Fig. A.2. Polyphase Duplex (Keuffel & Esser Co., trademark)

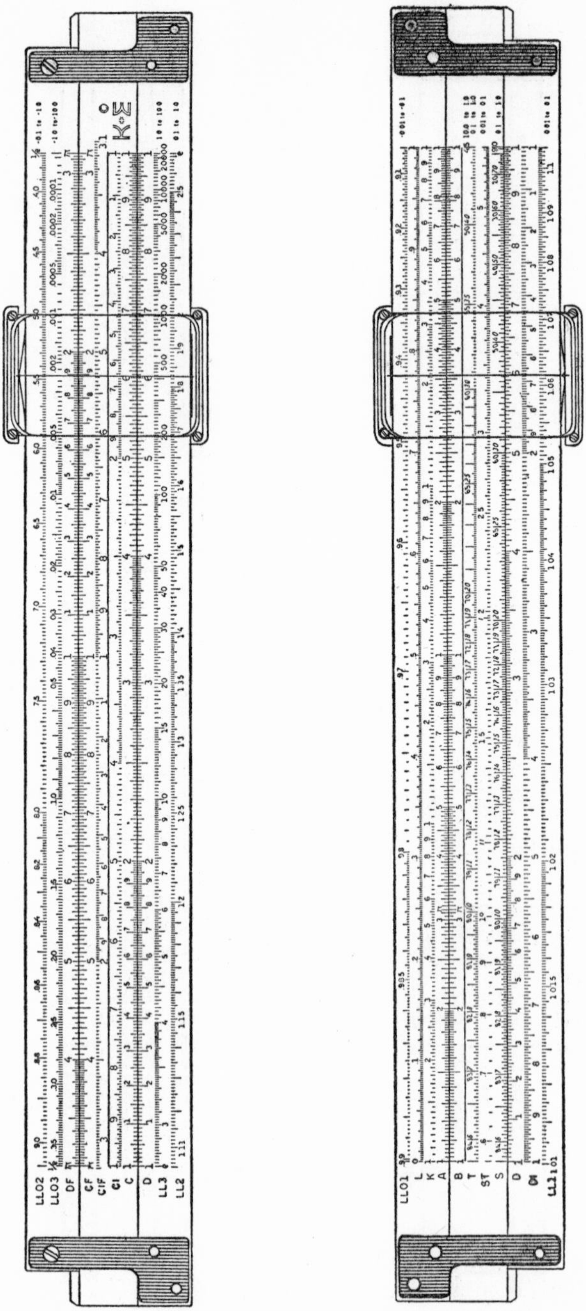

(Courtesy, Keuffel & Esser Co.)

(front)   (back)

Fig. A.3. LogLog Duplex Decitrig (Keuffel & Esser Co.,
trademark)

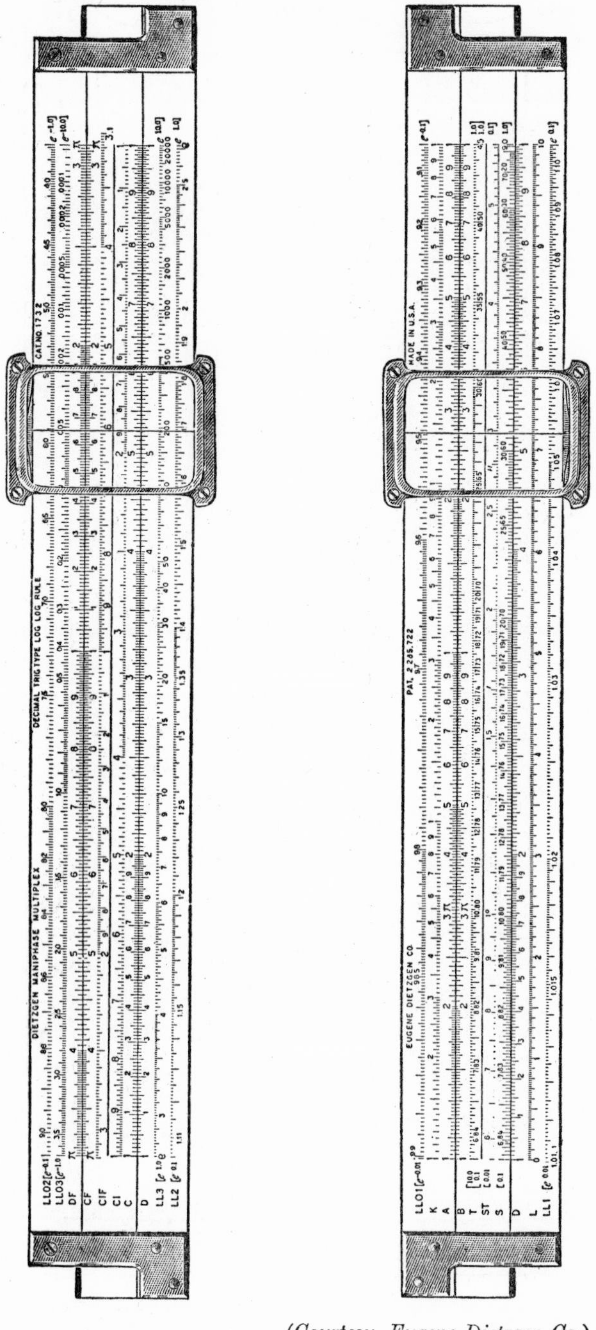

(Courtesy, Eugene Dietzgen Co.)

(front)   (back)

Fig. A.4. Maniphase Multiplex Decimal Trig (Eugene Dietzgen Co., trademark)

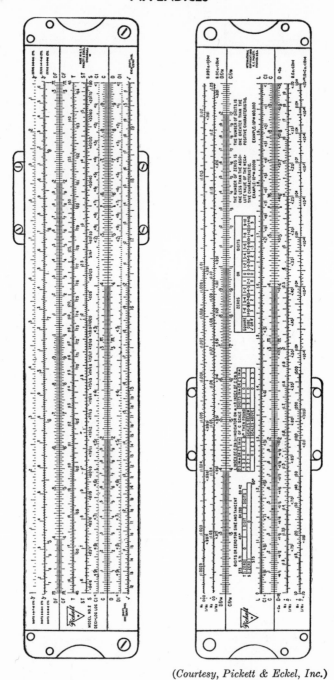

(front)   (back)

Fig. A.5. Deci-LogLog, Model No. 2. (Pickett & Eckel, Inc., trademark)

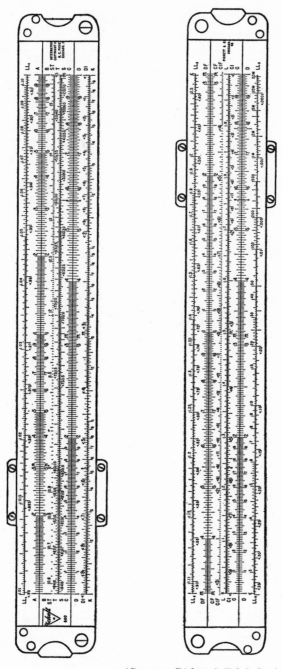

(Courtesy, Pickett & Eckel, Inc.)

(front) (back)

Fig. A.6. Model 800 (Pickett & Eckel Inc., trademark)

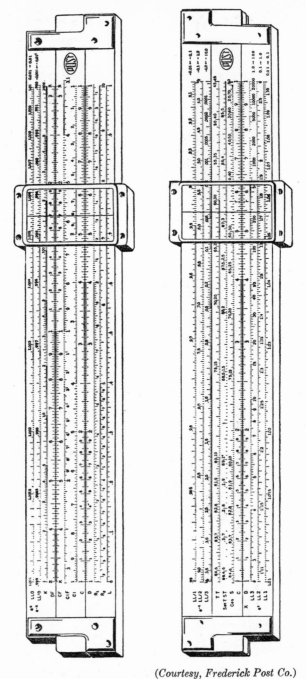

(Courtesy, Frederick Post Co.)

(front)   (back)

Fig. A.7. Versalog (Frederick Post Co., trademark)

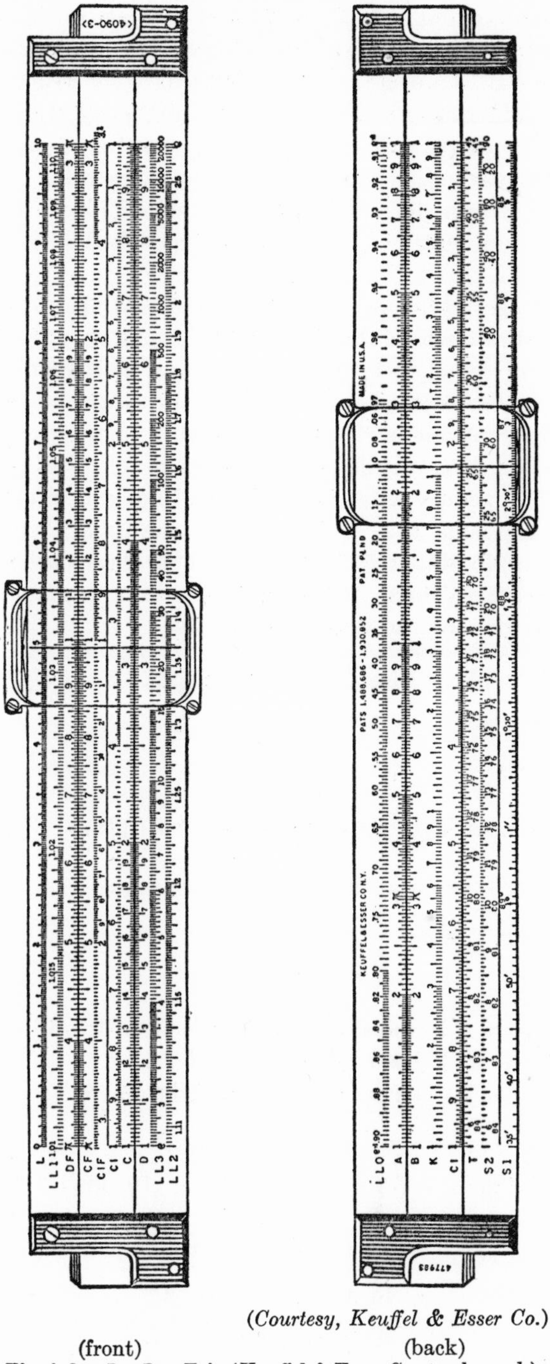

(Courtesy, Keuffel & Esser Co.)

(front)   (back)
Fig. A.8.   LogLog Trig (Keuffel & Esser Co., trademark)

A.2. Scale Equations. It is mentioned several times in the pages of this book that the straight slide rule operates by subtracting, adding, or equating lengths. Thus, if the functions used for constructing the various scales of a slide rule are known, these can be subtracted, added, or equated in accordance with the particular operation used, as a means for determining the equations solvable on that slide rule. And also, it is possible with certain slide rules to interchange slides. The above procedure will determine the types of problems solvable on such a hybrid slide rule.

The operating statements given in the several chapters are intended as a guide to those whose mathematical training may be limited at the time the use of the slide rule is studied. As mathematical knowledge increases, more abbreviated operating statements are understandable, and may be more convenient. Hence, operating instructions in the form of the scale equations can be put on one page for all of the commercial slide rules of Appendix A.1. If these equations are transformed, eliminating the logarithms, they will be in the more usual form.

Several examples illustrate the way in which these tables may be used.

If numbers are set on an LL2 scale and reading is made on a D scale, equating the two construction equations gives

$$\log (10 \ln N) = \log X;$$

or

$$10 \ln N = X$$

which if written with the scale names as subscripts is

$$\ln N_{LL2} = 0.1 X_D$$

or

$$e^{0.1X} = N$$

The basic range of X in the scale equations is from 1 to 10; or for numbers on the LL2 scale ln N lies between 0.1 and 1.0.

If lengths on an S scale are added to lengths on an A scale and the sum read on LL3

$$\log (\ln N) = \frac{1}{2} \log X + \log (10 \sin A°)$$

or

$$\ln N = 10 X^{\frac{1}{2}} \sin A°$$
$$N_{LL3} = e^{10\sqrt{X_A}} \sin A_S$$

The basic range of X on the A scale is from 1 to 100.

Logarithmic Scales[1]

Scale Name	Construction Equation	Scale Name	Construction Equation
C, D	$\log X$	$R_1, \sqrt{}$ (Low)	$2 \log X$
CF, DF	$\log X + \log \pi$	$R_2, \sqrt{}$ (High)	$2(\log X - \log \sqrt{10})$
CF/M, DF/M	$\log X - \log e$	K	$\frac{1}{3} \log X$
CI, DI	$\log 10 - \log X$	$\sqrt[3]{}$ (Low)	$3 \log X$
CIF	$\log \dfrac{10}{\pi} - \log X$	$\sqrt[3]{}$ (Middle)	$3(\log X - \log \sqrt[3]{10})$
A, B	$\frac{1}{2} \log X$	$\sqrt[3]{}$ (High)	$3(\log X - \log \sqrt[3]{100})$

Trigonometric Scales[2]

Scale Name	Construction Equation	Scale Name	Construction Equation
*S	$\frac{1}{2} \log (100 \sin A°)$	S, S2 (comp.)	$\log (10 \cos A°)$
ST, S1	$\log (100 \sin A°)$	T (direct) 6°–45°	$\log \tan A°$
ST, S1 (comp.)	$\log (100 \cos A°)$	†T (direct) 45°–84°	$\log (0.1 \tan A°)$
S, S2	$\log (10 \sin A°)$	T (comp.) 45°–84°	$- \log \tan A°$

* Figs. A.1, A.2.   † Fig. A.5.

Uniform and LogLog Scales[3]

Scale Name	Construction Equation	Scale Name	Construction Equation
L	N	LL2	$\pm \log (10 \ln N)$
N_4	$\log \log N$	N_2	$\log (100 \log N)$
LL3	$\log \ln N$	LL1	$\log (100 \ln N)$
$1/N_4$	$- \log \log N$	$1/N_2$	$- \log (100 \log N)$
LL03, LL/3	$- \log \ln N$	LL01, LL/1	$- \log (100 \ln N)$
LL_3	$\pm \log \ln N$	LL_1	$\pm \log (100 \ln N)$
N_3	$\log (10 \log N)$	*LL0	$\log (1000 \ln N)$
LL2	$\log (10 \ln N)$	LL/0	$- \log (1000 \ln N)$
$1/N_3$	$- \log (10 \log N)$	†LL0 (left)	$- \frac{1}{2} \log (100 \ln N)$
LL02, LL/2	$- \log (10 \ln N)$	LL00	$- \frac{1}{2} \log (100 \ln N)$

* Fig. A.7.   † Fig. A.8.

[1] Decimal point in X may be moved at will when operating with other logarithmic scales.

[2] The decimal point may not be moved in angle values except for small angles on the direct sine scales.

[3] The decimal point may not be moved in numbers on the LogLog scales.

A.3. Adjusting and Cleaning the Slide Rule. When purchased, the slide rule should be in adjustment and should be clean. It is undesirable to tinker with it unless necessary.

If the slide rule is dropped it may be knocked out of adjustment. Occasionally, weather changes make adjustments necessary. Sometimes, though rarely, screws work loose and require tightening.

The accuracy of alignment and looseness of the slide should be checked first. If the bracket screws on a duplex slide rule, Fig. A.9, are loosened,

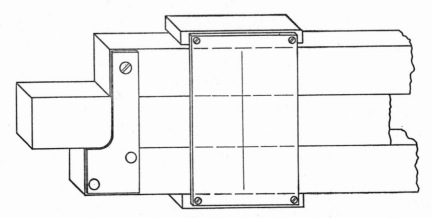

Fig. A.9. Duplex Slide Rule Showing Bracket Screws

the upper bar of the frame may be moved slightly to change the separation of the bars, or lengthwise to align scales on slide and frame. If adjustment of separation only is required, it is best to loosen one end at a time; the alignment is then not disturbed. The separation should be adjusted to permit easy movement and setting of the slide, and yet the friction should be enough to prevent slide movement, unless it is intentional.

Sometimes it is possible to overcome warping of the shorter bar of the frame. Loosen the bracket screws; spring the bar more than is necessary to make it straight; tighten the screws while holding the bar in the sprung position.

The hairlines should be checked after the frame is adjusted. If hairlines on both sides do not line up with end graduations, it may be possible to loosen the four screws in one glass only and move that glass a little to obtain alignment. At times only two screws on front and back of one corner of the glasses need be loosened to adjust the hairlines. If all eight screws in the runner are loosened at once, it is much more difficult to get both hairlines lined up to match the end graduations on both sides. As graduations to check the hairline with, the indexes on the D, A, R, $\sqrt{}$, and K scales should line up with π on the DF scale and 0 on an L scale. Also, e and $1/e$ on the LogLog scales should be aligned.

If a slide rule is in adjustment and it is necessary to clean under the glass, remove only one glass and slip the runner off the frame.

A damp cloth is suitable for cleaning a slide rule. Erasers or chemical means are undesirable because they may damage the surface and make the graduations less distinct.

Lubrication of the slide rule should not be necessary. Once in a while for wood-base slide rules, talcum powder in the grooves may be helpful. For metal slide rules, carbon from a soft pencil may serve the same purpose.

Adjustment of the Mannheim-type slide rule is easier than for the duplex rules. If the frame is adjustable, there are usually four screws as shown in the partial drawing, Fig. A.10. These screws may be loosened

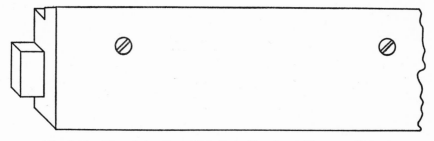

Fig. A.10. Mannheim-Type Slide Rule Showing Adjustment Screws

one or more at a time to change the separation of the upper bar on the frame. If endwise movement of the bar is needed, all four screws must be loosened at once.

The glass can often be adjusted on a Mannheim-type slide rule in much the same way as for the duplex rule. The fewer screws and only one glass make this a simpler task. The glass usually will slide off the end without dissassembly, making it easy to clean on a Mannheim-type slide rule.

A.4. Answers to Problems

Chapter 1

1.7. Scale Reading

	1A	1B	1C	1D	1E
a	5.00	2.50	9.09	9.90	9.95
c	1.25	1.26	1.65	1.515	2.43
e	7.70	2.34	3.16	1.063	4.72
g	1.75	7.14	3.40	4.60	1.96

1.12. Division

	1F	1G	1H	1I	1J
a	1.75	1.64	1.383	4.14	32.3
c	0.550	24.0	0.131	0.0403	0.239
e	850	0.227	233.5	626	0.001285
g	3000	0.247	0.0306	0.0557	48.1
i	5240	614	86.2	918	188
k	142	0.00717	170	0.000228	384

1.14. Multiplication

	1K	1L	1M	1N
a	5.10	9.30	6.21	36.7
c	910	6.25	3.025	0.0834
e	0.0975	30,900	755	11.0
g	270	27.0	0.0131	4.00
i	1010	209	213,000	464
k	281	463	286,700	27,600
m	0.00412	0.00155	6370	100,500
o	2.48×10^6	94.1	302	5.18
q	3.92×10^6	878	7570	52.1
s	0.00764	0.0112	2470	373,000

1.17. Continued Division and Multiplication

	1P	1Q	1R
a	1.24	3.52	3.00
c	0.536	0.0321	0.02565
e	0.00209	10.23	1.067
g	187.5	4.68	1.99
i	0.0920	707	222
k	1.327	0.2375	0.184
m	2.66	0.1274	129
o	42,000	3.72×10^6	2990

1.22. On Chapter 1

	1S	1T	1U	1V
a	1.0985	835.0	1.149	0.014585
c	617.06	10.564	38.71	749.7
e	0.00190	1.075	12.2	113.7×10^{-6}
g	3.33	253	0.267	52.8

	1S	1T	1U	1V
i	5.91	0.958	1280	1000
k	305	762	10,860	106.8
m	0.01693	0.01034	0.0189	0.00200
o	13.5	45.0	158×10^{-6}	1.14
q	91,200	0.205	1.097	304,000
s	0.643	63.5×10^{6}	1.375×10^{-6}	63.0

1W

a $U = 0.518; V = 7.28; W = 0.133$
c $U = 0.001587; V = 40,200; W = 163,300$

e 5.33; 0.300; 14.67; 123
g 96.8; 386.5; 760; 200

i 0.0322; 99.5; 0.270; 0.00944
k 0.00953; 0.003545; 653×10^{-6}; 0.0906

Chapter 2

2.5. Squares and Square Roots

	2A	2B	2C	2D
a	1.5625	0.406	0.0757	12.48
c	0.240	20.9	20.4	7.085
e	114.3	0.054	0.552	0.4857
g	81.9	2.046	2.31×10^{-4}	32.93
i	0.1537	35.06	1304	0.0768
k	604,000	9.62	467×10^{-6}	10.54
m	7.84×10^{-6}	5.665	0.0219	1.455
o	661	29.9	67.7	16.22

2.8. Cubes and Cube Roots

	2E	2F	2G	2H
a	14.17	1.026	381	2.02
c	0.001406	5.595	0.576	7.88
e	710	0.229	0.225	0.806
g	812,000	17.4	266	0.1932
i	531×10^{-6}	33.9	33.7	12.52
k	1.26×10^{6}	4.11	1906	2.122
m	98.0	0.461	620×10^{6}	5.39
o	13.48	2.587	0.139	0.0646

2.12. On Chapter 2

	2I	2J	2K
a	16.383	2.8755	49.215
c	1.8697	0.394	1.195
e	19.559	74.52	0.742
g	675	0.45267	1.054
i	56.31	2.064	6.625
k	4.718	8.46	3.06
m	40.7	14.8	3.235
o	1275	3.36	8.20

Chapter 3

3.6. Sines and Cosines

	3A	3B	3C	3D	3E
a	0.500	0.939	0.0401	0.01163	0.987
c	0.292	0.0262	0.660	0.613	0.1563
e	0.629	0.00384	0.00297	0.891	−0.995
g	48.6°	13.3°	201.75°	0.38 rad	7.0°
i	53.5°	4.70°	180.8°	1.017 rad	21.2°
k	9.5°	0.40°	182.12°	0.0802 rad	14.8°
m	26.8°	0.35°	234.2°	1.326 rad	2.7°
o	0.500	0.0784	0.22	0.344	0.94
q	0.682	0.01745	0.0314	0.0209	−0.99
s	0.208	0.950	0.464	0.99	−0.98
u	68.0°	88.0°	115°	1.277 rad	18°
w	82.0°	79.0°	96.6°	1.654 rad	85.0°

3.9. Tangents and Cotangents

	3F	3G	3H	3I	3J
a	0.249	1.19	2.646	0.949	−0.364
c	0.7265	0.625	15.97	1.26	−0.649
e	0.096	2.356	1.437	0.070	0.364
g	32.0°	17.0°	39.3°	0.346 rad	65.75°
i	52.0°	83.5°	108.0°	1.043 rad	40.7°
k	48.0°	88.0°	125.0°	2.78 rad	82.4°
m	13.25	6.90	1.745	0.0349	0.532
o	22.0	2.42	12.5	0.136	0.675

	3F	3G	3H	3I	3J
q	38.2°	4.24°	1.536 rad	78.15°	65.3°
s	70.2°	5.12°	0.634 rad	86.56°	37.6°

3.14. On Chapter 3

	3K	3L	3M	3N
a	1.004	1.023	16.4	6.22
c	5.75	43.0	1.035	2.71
e	85.76°	88.79°	30.7°	3.7°
g	83.9°	29.7°	1.53°	13.77°

	3K	3L
i	$b:72; c:75.3$	$A:31.4°; c:100$
k	$B:20°; c:0.938$	$b:135.3; c:155$
m	$b:3.94; c:56.34$	$B:9.95°; b:521.95$
o	$a:7.76; c:10.3$	$c:59.6; b:59.5$

	3P	3Q
a	$c:22.8; A:29.4°; C:110.6°$	$c:42; A:17.5°; B:67.5°$
c	$a:2.79; c:0.875; A:100°$	$a:13.7; c:71.9; B:50.5°$
e	$b:146.5; B:168.67°; C:7.33°$	$a:15.2; B:78°; C:57°$
g	$b:140.5; c:115; B:120°$	$a:44.8; c:58.1; C:48°$
i	$c:97.2; B:60.5°; C:70°$	$c:57.7; A:12.3°; C:130.8°$
k	$a:21.9; b:7.75; A:101.5°$	$b:74.9; A:3.67°; C:89.2°$

	3R	3S	3T
a	0.076	0.466	0.217
c	40.9	1.76	10.55
e	0.987	0.972	0.916
g	0.0373	0.265	5.88
i	0.757, etc.	14.13, etc.	0.0152, etc.
k	22.5, etc.	48.25, etc.	156, etc.

Chapter 4

4.3. Logarithms

	4A	4B	4C	4D
a	0.342	9.806 − 10	3.433	7.964 − 10
c	2.274	8.466 − 10	1.544	8.613 − 10
e	1.82	0.148	1130	0.0263
g	86.7	0.436	575	0.00363

	4A	4B	4C	4D
i	0.336	−2.50	8.57	−1.01
k	6.33	−0.0725	6.44	−4.96
m	24.5	0.198	2.90	35×10^4
o	1.19	0.440	19,000	0.9607

4.5. Powers and Roots

	4E	4F	4G	4H
a	15.5	0.396	3.42	0.0002
c	41.5	0.0008	5.70	0.4925
e	2.99	0.9264	1.518	0.883
g	1.174	0.005	1.0334	1.0965
i	1.01635	0.9262	1.01465	0.534
k	23,000	0.9657	120	3.05×10^{-5}
m	41.0	71.0	0.038	16×10^{-8}
o	1.223	1.26	0.9917	0.614

4.11. On Chapter 4

	4I	4J	4K	4L
a	3.04	3.32	0.864	0.9893
c	0.388	1.083	0.828	0.458
e	110	770	36.6	0.0437
g	0.940	1.125	0.56	0.9671
i	4.38	380	24.7	412
k	900	2.9425	0.226	1.517

INDEX